Maggie, Holly, & Susie —
thanks for visiting beautiful
coastal Alaska with us!
Steve MacLean
August, 2010

Familiar Plants
of Coastal Alaska

Stephen MacLean

D1593540

Greatland Graphics
Anchorage, Alaska
www.alaskacalendars.com

About the Author

Steve MacLean has been an Alaskan since 1963. He was a member of the faculty of the University of Alaska Fairbanks until he retired in 1997. He now spends half of each year traveling to Antarctica, the Arctic, and coastal Alaska as a ship-based naturalist. When he is not away on a ship he still resides in Alaska.

All photos are by the author except where noted.

Front cover:
Alpine Sweetvetch along the Alsek River, Glacier Bay National Park (photo by Michael DeYoung/ AlaskaStock.com).

Title page:
Shootingstars and Alaska lupine, Baranof Island.

Contents page:
Dwarf fireweed at Pederson Lagoon, Kenai Fjords National Park (photo by Edward Bovy).

Back cover:
Expedition ship in Misty Fiords National Monument (photo by Michael Nolan/Wildlife Images); hikers at Ideal Creek, Mitkoff Island; Alaska lupine, Bartlett Cove, Glacier Bay National Park; kinnikinnick, western buttercup and dwarf nagoonberry.

Familiar Plants of Coastal Alaska
ISBN 978-0-9821896-7-2
Printed in China

©2010 Greatland Graphics
PO Box 141414
Anchorage, AK 99514 USA
www.alaskacalendars.com

Acknowledgments

Lindblad Expeditions has made it possible for me to visit so much of Southeast Alaska and share it with a most excellent group of travelers. I thank the many who graciously tolerated my photographic distractions on their shore excursions.

Alissa Crandall, Vance Gese, Mike Greenfelder, Stephen Handley, Bette Lu Krause, Emily Mount, Norio Matsumoto, and Michael Nolan contributed photos. Gretchen Pedersen gave the manuscript a thorough and careful review when it was much needed. Dr. David Murray brought me up to date on developments in the naming of Alaskan plants. Thanks to family, friends and colleagues, too numerous to mention individually, for their encouragement. Edward Bovy of Greatland Graphics turned an idea into a reality.

This book is for Gwen, as she grows up surrounded by the beauty of Alaska.

CONTENTS

About this book

For more than twenty years I have been fortunate to spend at least part of each summer immersed in the natural wonders of Southeast Alaska. Sometimes the experience has included the coastline between Alaska and Puget Sound, following the Inside Passage along the east side of Vancouver Island. I do this as a naturalist with Lindblad Expeditions. The company offers "expedition travel", using small ships and emphasizing the natural world of its destinations. The job of a naturalist is to provide education, interpret nature, encourage and answer questions, lead our guests on hikes ashore and on excursions in small inflatable boats, and convince them that they are having the most fun they have ever had in the most wonderful of places. It is an easy job.

The ships that we use (see back cover) are small and shallow draft, able to poke into small coves and bays in search of bears feeding in coastal meadows, bald eagles nesting in towering coastal trees, sea otters rafting in the bays, and whales exploiting the rich marine productivity. We find all of these and more. My self-appointed task is to encourage our guests to see beyond the charismatic large birds and mammals, beyond the majesty of mountains and glaciers, to admire the small but beautiful parts of wild Alaska; to get down on hands and knees and peer into the private parts of the flowers that appear so profusely during the short, intense northern summer.

My approach to nature observation in Alaska changed dramatically with the advent of digital photography. In the pre-digital world, we accumulated canisters of exposed film for later processing. Only upon returning home did we receive feedback, and then it was too late to take advantage of the naturalist to say: "What is this yellow flower?" In the digital era, there is instant gratification, whether on the LCD screen on the back of the camera or on a laptop computer or other download device. You can admire your many good shots and reject the occasional bad ones. I was hooked!

I began accumulating plant pictures to share with our guests and assist them in their identifications, posting a photo and bit of text describing the "Plant of the Day" on the ship's bulletin board. This book grew, plant by plant, from that effort. Its purpose is to assist visitors in identifying the plants that they are likely to encounter in the various habitats of the Temperate Rainforest, especially in coastal Alaska.

Let me say what this book is not.

(1) It is not a catalog of the plants of coastal Alaska. There is no attempt to capture all of the plant species that grow in the Temperate Rainforest. Rather, these are the plants that visitors most frequently encounter on excursions ashore, the ones that most catch the eye. Grasses and sedges are particularly underrepresented; I show only a few of the most frequent and distinctive species.

(2) It is not a book of plant keys. A key is a series of questions concerning plant structure; the correct answers lead you to identification of the plant. Use of keys requires knowledge of plant anatomy and the associated botanical vocabulary and, often, a microscope or other magnifier to see the relevant characters. Instead of keys, this book offers photographs and succinct descriptions as a guide to identification.

(3) Despite the word "plant" in the title, the book is not restricted to the plants. Familiar mushrooms and lichens are included as well. I am well aware that fungi and lichens are not really plants, but they will be encountered on any plant-oriented excursion and they generate similar interest.

The book is an attempt to encourage visitors to look closely, to admire the wonderful diversity of plants and plant-like organisms of the Temperate Rainforest and to attach names to the things that they see and admire, both visually and photographically.

How to use this book

The organization of the book may not be immediately obvious to all users. I steadfastly reject the notion of organization by flower color. That approach ignores plants that do not have conspicuous flowers, either because of time of season or because they just don't, and it often places closely related plants in widely separate chapters. Also, judging flower color is not always as easy at it should be. Sometimes flowers of the same species are of several colors or they may change color as they develop, and some of us find it difficult to separate pink from magenta from purple.

In this book, groups are placed in an evolutionary relationship (Table C, page 207) until the level of plant Family is reached; the families are then arranged alphabetically. Biologists commonly find Family to be an intuitive and useful level of organization. Recognizing Family-level characteristics is a valuable skill. Relationships within the plant kingdom are best indicated by the flowers. Non-floral attributes like plant stature and leaf size and shape are easily changed evolutionarily. Flower characters like number and organization of reproductive parts are much more stable and likely to reveal true relatedness.

If you recognize the family, Table C will take you where you want to go. But if you do not recognize plant families and don't want to try, fear not; we have an alternative for you.

The somewhat daunting-looking Table D (page 208) is actually quite simple. If you can see flower color and you can count petals or otherwise assess flower arrangement, Table D should lead you to a list of likely possibilities. At that point go to the pictures and, hopefully, you will find your plant.

Where flowers of the same species may have different colors, they are included in both color columns of the table so no arbitrary decision is necessary. If you recognize the family, so much the better: the list of possibilities becomes much shorter, but this is not necessary.

Finally, there is the navigational technique of turning pages until something looks familiar, but I hope that users will give the tables a try.

A bit of the Temperate Rainforest growing atop a sea stack, Kenai Fjords National Park. The large trees are Sitka spruce.

Plant names

Like many other organisms, plants have both common and scientific names. Unfortunately, you will often find multiple names for the same plant in each of these categories. There is no arbiter of common names in the plant kingdom. The American Ornithologists' Union has standardized common names of North American birds, and the British Ornithologists' Union has done the same globally, but no such organization exists for plants. Common names often differ regionally, and even in the same area, multiple common names may be used. Hence, for many of the species in this book, two or even three common names are in use and so are given.

Scientific names are another matter; they are meant to be systematic and adhere to a fixed set of rules. The species name is assigned by the person who first recognizes the plant as new to science and describes it in a published report. The describer, recognizing similarities, will assign the plant to an existing genus; or, if the new species is sufficiently different from all other described species, a new genus will be erected with its own name. Our system of classification is hierarchical. Different species of the same genus are more similar and more closely related than are species of different genera. A group of related genera forms a family, and members of the same family are closer to one another than they are to any of the species of different families, etc.. While each species has its own unique place in the complete hierarchy of organization—species, genus, family, order, class, and phylum—we usually refer to an organism with the binomial of Genus name (capitalized) and species name (not capitalized). Scientific names are placed in italics (as in this book) or underlined.

Scientific names are rendered in Latin or latinized Greek. For instance, the species name must agree in number and gender with the genus name, following the rules of Latin grammar. Many scientific names are descriptive of some feature of the plant. The sundew species *Drosera rotundifolia* has round leaves, *Vaccinium ovalifolium* has oval-shaped leaves, and the species name *trifoliata* is applied to species of the genera *Menyanthes* and *Tiarella*, both with leaves that divide into three leaflets. The scientific name *Oplopanax horridus* is pretty darn descriptive of devil's club, a plant with very nasty spines.

Names can be geographic (e.g. Sitka spruce (*Picea sitchensis*), Alaska blueberry (*Vaccinium alaskaense*), northern twinflower (*Linnaea borealis*)). Yet other species names are honorific, recognizing some prominent botanist or, perhaps the person who found the new plant. *Spiraea douglasii* is named for David Douglas (1798-1834), a Scottish naturalist and botanical explorer, and the name of Archibald Menzies (1754-1842), the cantankerous Scottish naturalist on George Vancouver's voyage of exploration (1791-95), reverberates through the list of plant species of the Northwest Coast (as in *Menziesia ferruginea*.) (Eric Hultén, in his classic and comprehensive work on Alaskan plant taxonomy [1968], added "subspecies *menziesii*" to **Spiraea douglasii** and thus he got them both.) But one never, never names a plant after oneself.

There is at least one other source of species names: Latinized whimsy. Entomologists, having many more species to name, seem especially prone to flights of whimsy. I highly recommend a perusal of "A Fly Called Aiyaiyai" by Susan Milnus, published in the May 26, 2001 issue of *Science News*. You can find it by entering the title into your internet search engine. Trust me; it is worth it. Botanists may be a bit more stodgy. I cannot find any cases of whimsy in the plant names reported in this book.

Scientific names are not quite as fixed as we might wish. Names change based upon new research and new sources of information. Studies may show that populations of a named species deserve status as separate species, or that species once considered distinct should be treated as variants of the same species. Similarly, genera may be lumped or divided, and species might be moved from one genus to another. I have tried to use the latest names, but I have included other names under which the species might be listed in previous publications. This is not entirely consistent with the more precise use of the term "synonym" in a botanical treatise, but I think it serves our purpose.

The Climate

There is a reason why we call it a Temperate Rainforest (and why good quality rain gear and waterproof boots are essential for your trip.) Temperate Rainforest is found around the globe in both the northern and southern hemispheres. It is always on the western side of continents and large islands in the Temperate Zone: the Northwest Coast of North America, the British Isles and Scandinavian coast, Chilean Patagonia, and New Zealand. It is there because of global wind patterns. The prevailing winds of the Temperate Zone are the Westerlies that blow from west to east, hence from ocean to land on west coasts.

Water, so familiar to us, is really a very remarkable substance. One of its unusual properties is its very high specific heat, a property that relates temperature change to energy exchange. Simply put, compared with other substances, a lot of energy is gained or lost as water warms and cools. Thus, water changes temperature only slowly. The energy absorbed in summer does not translate into much warming, and the energy given off in winter results in relatively little cooling.

The same property influences day/night changes; water warms up rather little in daytime and cools off little at night. The result is temperate conditions—not very hot in summer, not very cold in winter; not too hot in the daytime, and not too cold in the early morning. We use the term Maritime Climate to describe climates that are moderated by their proximity to a large body of water.

On the other side, the east side of land masses at the same latitudes (e.g. the Atlantic side of North America), the prevailing Westerly winds have passed over land with a specific heat that is only about one fourth that of the ocean. The land heats up easily making summers hot, but winters are much colder and the daily variation in temperature, in both summer and winter, is greater.

Climates that take their character from the land rather than water are called Continental Climates. The west coast is maritime in nature; the east coast and the interior of the continent are much more continental. On a more local scale, this phenomenon produces the "lake effect" that is seen in comparing the west and east sides of the Great Lakes.

Winter sea ice off eastern North America reaches all the way to the Gulf of Saint Lawrence at about 45° N. In contrast, the Pacific

Ocean and Alaska's Inside Passage remain ice-free and navigable to above 60° N, more than 1,000 miles further north than in the Atlantic. In Alaska, sea ice forms only in deep fjords that cut into the continent away from the moderating effect of the ocean, and even here the ice is more ephemeral than seasonal. (Warning: do not confuse sea ice with the freshwater ice that is transported down from the mountains by glaciers. Glaciers that reach tidewater may calve many tons of ice each day into a fjord, thus clogging it with bergs of various sizes, but this is fresh-water ice that originated over land.)

That, briefly, takes care of the "temperate" part. What about the "rain" of the Rainforest? As the winds pass over the ocean, water evaporates and the air becomes saturated with vapor. Storm systems develop and move generally eastward on the prevailing

	Jan max temp	Jan min temp	July max temp	July min temp	Annual Precipitation
West Coast					
Ketchikan 55° 21' N	39°	28°	65°	51°	152.4 in
Sitka 57° 03' N	39°	31°	61°	52°	86.1 in
Juneau 58° 21' N	31°	21°	64°	49°	58.3 in
Haines 59° 14' N	29°	19°	66°	51°	47.8 in
East Coast					
Nain, Labrador 56° 50' N	7°	-9°	59°	41°	35.1 in
Interior					
Whitehorse, B.C. 60° 43' N	8°	-8°	69°	46°	10.5 in

Table A. A comparison of temperature (°F) and precipitation at locations in Coastal Alaska, a comparable latitude on the east coast of North America, and at an inland (British Columbia) site.

westerly winds. Within a storm, air circulates in a counterclockwise direction (in the northern hemisphere) around the lowest pressure—the deeper the low, the stronger the winds. Thus, even in the zone of prevailing Westerlies, we can encounter winds from all directions, depending on the current location of the nearest low.

Most frequently, Pacific storms strike Coastal Alaska with winds from the southwest. When these winds encounter land, the air is deflected upward and rises. Rising air is under less pressure so it expands, and as it expands it cools. This process is called adiabatic cooling. (The principle of adiabatic cooling or cooling by expansion is used in your refrigerator or air conditioner. Air is compressed at the compressor and allowed to expand within the coils, thus cooling them.)

Colder air can hold less moisture. Excess moisture, beyond saturation, condenses and falls as rain or snow. Tall mountains that intercept and deflect moist marine breezes give us abundant precipitation, especially on the windward side. Air that crosses the mountains to reach the leeward side has already lost some of its moisture. As the air descends it warms and its capacity to hold moisture increases, so areas removed from the immediate coast get less precipitation than the outer coast. However, as the centers of low pressure move (you can follow this on a weather chart) leading wind directions change, so all areas of the Temperate Rainforest are sometimes the recipients of this precipitation. All areas are wet, but some are wetter than others. The wetter areas are near the outer coast (e.g. Sitka and Ketchikan); the less wet areas (I dare not say drier) are farther from the coast. Juneau and Haines receive less precipitation than Ketchikan and Sitka because they are behind the first tier of coastal mountains that are on the large islands of Baranof, Chichagof and Admiralty (the "ABC Islands" of Southeast Alaska) and the mainland surrounding Glacier Bay.

The wettest spot in Alaska is Little Port Walter, on the south coast of Baranof Island. It receives an average of more than 220 inches of precipitation annually and no month receives less than 8 inches. On a single day in 1955, more than 10 inches of rain fell there.

A boardwalk trail through the Old Growth Forest at Ideal Creek, Mitkoff Island. Note the abundant shrub and herb layers in the vegetation. The large-leaved plant is skunk cabbage (p. 87).

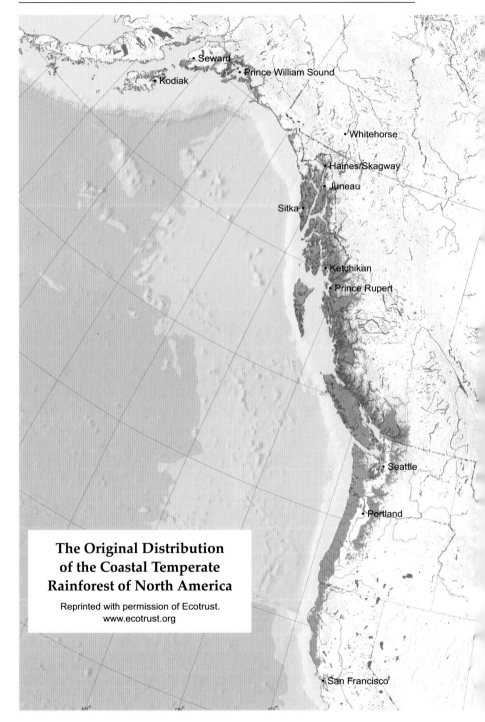

**The Original Distribution
of the Coastal Temperate
Rainforest of North America**

Reprinted with permission of Ecotrust.
www.ecotrust.org

The Temperate Rainforest

Temperate Rainforest is a community type that has developed independently in different parts of the world with similar climate. It is not defined by particular plant species but by the combination of plant growth forms, the aspect of the forest. The Temperate Rainforest of the Pacific Northwest occurs all the way from Northern California through the coastal parts of Oregon, Washington and British Columbia, to Alaska's Prince William Sound, part of Cook Inlet, the Kenai Peninsula, and Kodiak Island.

Species richness is higher in the southern part of this distribution, but most of the species of the Rainforest in Alaska are also components of the forest farther south. The version of the Temperate Rainforest that occupies Southeast Alaska is best referred to as Coastal Spruce-Hemlock Forest.

Beginning in British Columbia Douglas-fir becomes a dominant tree, and species of pine and true firs (as opposed to Douglas-fir, which is not a fir at all) enter the forest as well. In Northern California we find stands of Temperate Rainforest dominated by immense Coast Redwoods.

Despite these species differences, the structure of the forest remains much the same. In part, the continuity of the North American Temperate Rainforest over many degrees of latitude is a result of the North Pacific Current, which flows from west to east across the Pacific Ocean. When it strikes North America, it divides. Part flows southward as the California Current and part flows northward as the Alaska Current, taking North Pacific water of similar temperature in both directions.

Forest habitat

Evergreen coniferous trees dominate the tree layer of the Temperate Rainforest. In Coastal Alaska these are Sitka spruce, Western and mountain hemlocks, Western red cedar, and Alaska or yellow cedar (pages 79-84). Broad-leaved deciduous tree species are few and mainly restricted to riparian (streamside) stands and to successional stands, as in areas cleared by logging. The biggest and tallest trees in all of North America are found in the Temperate Rainforest (Table B). Related to their size, they are long-lived, reaching from 500 to more than 1,000 years.

Why do trees of the Temperate Rainforest grow so large? One contributing factor is the absence of fire as a significant ecological factor. Where fire disturbance is low, as it is in the Rainforest, the trees are more often able to reach advanced age and express their full growth potential.

But that is only part of the story. Trees elsewhere, even if protected from fire, will not reach this size. Large size results when the plant invests its resources in lignin to grow a trunk. A trunk can be thought of as a leaf display device, a way to get photosynthetic tissue high up into the canopy. It is a way to outcompete your neighbors for light. If water or nutrients were the main growth-limiting factors we would expect the plant to invest more resources in acquiring these by growing an extensive root system. In the rainforest water is pretty much always available, and the conditions of moderate climate allow decomposition of dead organic matter

Species	Age	Diameter	Height
Sitka Spruce	> 700 yrs	8 ft	220 ft
Western Hemlock	> 1,000 yrs	5 ft	190 ft
Mountain Hemlock	> 500 yrs	3 ft	125 ft
Alaska Cedar	> 1,000 yrs	4 ft	100 ft
Western Red Cedar	> 1,000 yrs	5 ft	140 ft

Table B. Some characteristics of canopy-level trees of the Temperate Rainforest of Alaska
(after Viereck and Little: *Alaska Trees and Shrubs*; 2007).

Norio Matsumoto

One of the diagnostic characteristics of the Temperate Rainforest is an abundance of moss growing on the forest floor, fallen trees and the bases and branches of living trees.

to occur year-around, leading to rapid recycling of nutrients. The result is a relative plenty of both water and nutrients, favoring the investment of precious resources in competition for light.

Light is much more of a growth-limiting factor for small trees—seedlings and saplings growing in shade under the forest canopy. Spruce and hemlock use different growth strategies to reach the canopy. Spruce is a rapid-growing species, but in order to grow rapidly it requires access to ample resources, including light. There is too little light under a closed-canopy forest for spruce seedlings and saplings to grow. Hemlock, on the other hand, grows more slowly but it can do so under low light conditions, so hemlock recruitment can and does occur under an undisturbed forest canopy. When you walk through a closed-canopy forest you will see seedlings of hemlock but rarely of spruce. So how does spruce, intolerant of shade, remain in the forest? Read on.

There is one more stage in the life cycle of trees, beyond the seedlings, saplings and mature, canopy-level trees. This final stage consists of the old senescent, dying trees and dead snags that stand

Red squirrels are specialists on the seeds of Sitka spruce. They store large numbers of cones underground and feed on them during the winter. The scales of cones that have been consumed accumulate above the storage areas in large piles called squirrel middens.

(left) A large Sitka Spruce growing in an Old Growth Forest stand at Sitkoh Bay, Chichagof Island.

in the canopy. Because of the sheer size of the trunks, and because living trees protect themselves with compounds that deter insects and micro-organisms (think of the lovely scent of cedar wood), dead trees decay slowly and remain standing in the canopy for many years.

Some people will contend that dead, decomposing trees standing in the forest represent the waste of a resource that should have been harvested. They might even use the value-laden term "over-mature" for a forest with such trees. Nonsense! Such trees are a valuable—one could even say essential—part of the forest. When a canopy-level tree finally breaks and falls, usually during a winter storm, it often brings down other trees with it. This creates a local opening in the forest, a light gap, where new life flourishes. Some plants are light gap specialists that depend on openings for their recruitment. Sitka spruce is such a species. Successful spruce

Vance Gese

Moss-draped hemlock on Kodiak Island shade an understory of devil's club, lady fern, red huckleberry and other plants.

reproduction and recruitment into the forest occurs along forest edges and especially in light gaps where the canopy is broken. Death and fall of old trees keeps spruce in the forest. Devil's club (p. 113) is another light gap specialist.

The history of tree fall is reflected in the horizontal or patch diversity of the forest, with light gaps of different ages and stages of regeneration. Without deadfalls to create light gaps the forest would be much more homogeneous and, frankly, monotonous.

Once a dead tree falls it is quickly colonized by mosses. The moss acts as a trap for moisture, for detritus that decays and provides nutrients, and for seeds that fall from the canopy above. Conditions are perfect for seed germination and seedling growth. Seedlings growing here have access to more light than they would on the forest floor in competition with established plants, and so they have a distinct advantage. The dead tree becomes a nurse log or nursery log (both terms are used), supporting the growth of the next generation of trees. Over time the seedling (or, more accurately, some tiny proportion of the seedlings) becomes a sapling and sends down roots to the soil below. The nurse log gradually decomposes away, but the history of germination and early growth remains evident in the twisted, gnarly shape of the bases of the forest trees. Nurse logs are critical to forest regeneration. Use of nurse logs is not limited to trees. Red huckleberry (p. 140) is a forest shrub that commonly grows on nurse logs.

The Temperate Rainforest is rich in shrub species, particularly of the heath family, Ericaceae (pp. 135-146). This family includes the blueberries, cranberries, and huckleberry. Like the trees, shrub species differ in their tolerance of shade. Some grow successfully under a closed forest canopy; others require higher levels of light and are found in light gaps and other openings and along the forest edge. Most of the shrub species of the forest are deciduous (they drop their leaves each fall), but when we enter the muskeg bog habitat we find evergreen species that retain their leaves over the winter. From mid-July onward there is an extra reward for a walk through the forest as berries of the different shrub species reach their peak of delectable ripeness.

The bases of forest trees take their twisted and contorted shape from their germination and early growth on nurse logs.

Beneath the shrub layer there is a rich diversity of forest floor herbs. Thus, there is impressive structural or vertical height diversity in the forest, with an abundance of plant matter (biomass) at the forest floor, shrub, sapling, and canopy levels. Also on the forest floor and extending up the trunks and branches of trees are many ferns, mosses and lichens. In fact, the abundance and diversity of these organisms is one of the characteristic and diagnostic features of Temperate Rainforests wherever this community is found.

The forest that I have been describing is the Old Growth Forest. Old growth is the end point of forest development when a dynamic equilibrium has been reached and the forest is no longer undergoing directional change.

A tree has an age; a population of trees has an age distribution. During forest development, in the process that we call succession, the age distribution changes. It seems obvious enough that a young forest is dominated by young trees. As the forest develops and matures the trees grow older. Some die and younger trees enter the population to replace them. The age distribution of

Light streams through an opening in the forest canopy to produce a light-gap where new growth can flourish.

the tree population becomes more diverse. Eventually the forest contains a mixture of seedlings, saplings, mature, and senescent trees.

Seeds germinate. Some live, some die. A fortunate few grow through the several life stages, and a tiny fraction of the seeds survive long enough to reproduce. But the proportion of these life stages, the distribution of ages in the tree population, remains unchanged. Individual trees (or, for that matter, other plants) come and go, light gaps develop and are filled in, new gaps occur elsewhere, but the forest as a whole remains in a dynamic equilibrium. This is a key characteristic of Old Growth Forest.

Species composition also changes during forest succession. Colonizing species dominate early in the process; gradually, these are replaced by more competitive species. Once the old growth condition is reached the forest is at a dynamic equilibrium with respect to species composition. For example, the suite of plant species that specialize on light gaps might occur at a particular spot in the forest now and elsewhere in the forest one hundred years from now, but somewhere in the forest a new light gap has developed and elsewhere in the forest older light gaps are in various stages of succession. As long as the rate of light gap generation remains approximately constant the forest is in dynamic equilibrium and species composition over the forest as a whole is unchanging. This is another important characteristic of Old Growth Forest.

It is not a necessary feature of forest succession that living plant material continues to accumulate throughout succession, but it is true for the Temperate Rainforest. Biomass in the Old Growth Temperate Rainforest is enormous. Much of this is wood in the giant forest trees. It is debatable just how "alive" wood is, but by any measure—amount of green tissue, total plant biomass—the living tissue of the Temperate Rainforest is as high or higher than any ecosystem on earth. Foresters who are interested in commercial harvest measure the quantity of wood in thousands of board-feet-per-acre (bfa). High volume stands of the Temperate Rainforest exceed 50,000 bfa, with peak stands of more than 100,000 bfa—and that is a lot of wood. Stands with the highest timber volume occur at low elevation near the sea, and commonly near salmon spawning streams where the forest is fertilized by the remains of dead fish that have brought nutrients from the ocean;

A revegetating clear-cut along the shore of Sitkoh Bay, Chichagof Island. The complete process of forest succession to the Old-Growth stage takes hundreds of years.

the most productive forests thrive on nutrients of marine origin.

Second growth is a term used to describe forest in intermediate stages of succession, before the old growth condition is reached. In the Temperate Rainforest of North America second growth is most commonly found as regrowth following timber harvest. Most logging in Alaska is done by clear-cutting, where entire tracts of forest are harvested at the same time. Selective logging and helicopter logging are simply too expensive to be cost-effective, and they become even less feasible as the price of fuel rises.

In Second Growth Forest, the age and size distribution of the trees is more even than in old growth. This is especially so if the land was replanted following harvest. The trees germinated more or less together in both time and space, and they grow and age together. The trees grow close together as a dense stand with foliage concentrated at the same height. This blocks most of the light from penetrating to the ground level. Consequently, Second Growth Forest supports much less ground-layer vegetation and produces less food for wildlife. In contrast, the structurally complex canopy of the old growth allows more light to reach the ground, supporting more ground-level vegetation and making it important habitat for wildlife.

Second growth lacks the light gaps of old growth. Certainly, second growth trees die as they are outcompeted by their neighbors so the stands are self-thinning, but the trees are not of a size that their death creates significant light gaps. Compared with old growth, second growth forests are homogeneous in both the vertical and the horizontal dimensions.

How long does it take a forest to reach the old growth condition? A very long time. At least hundreds and perhaps more than a thousand years. It is more than just the life span of a single tree. Nobody has been there to watch a forest develop from initiation of succession through intermediate stages to old growth. This long development means that, in essence, Old Growth Forest is a non-renewable resource. Once the forest is cut the old growth condition will not be reached again in a time scale that is relevant to our own existence.

In the southern part of the North American Temperate Rainforest, in California, Oregon, and Washington, most of Old Growth Forest has been harvested; it is gone. That which remains is contained within land of protected status, parks and preserves of various sorts and sizes. What was once a continuous forest is now a set of more or less isolated patches or islands of habitat. In British Columbia about half of the Old Growth Forest remains.

Only in Alaska can we still find large, contiguous stands of Old Growth Temperate Rainforest, and even here a majority of the highest volume stands have fallen to the loggers' chainsaws.

Most of the forests of Southeast Alaska are contained within the Tongass National Forest. The forest is a *national* resource that is managed by the United States Forest Service, a branch of the U.S. Department of Agriculture. One can hardly visit Southeast Alaska without seeing evidence of clear-cutting. Suffice to say that there is considerable debate over management of the Tongass National Forest. Visitors and residents of Alaska alike will form their own opinions on this often-contentious subject.

A forest edge along the margins of a stream on northern Baranof
Island. Here, where light is abundant, shrubs flourish.

Forest edge habitat

There is a suite of species that characteristically occur along
edges where light is greater than under the forest canopy. This
includes the landward side of beaches, light gaps, avalanche
chutes, stream margins, and the interface between meadow and
forest. The most prominent edge species, and perhaps the most
widely distributed plant in coastal Alaska, is Sitka alder (p. 118).
Salmonberry (p. 191), thimbleberry (p. 192), and skunk cabbage
(p. 87) also fall into this group.

A muskeg bog of Petersburg Creek on Kupreanof Island, near Petersburg. The trees are shore pines, a characteristic of this habitat.

Muskeg bog habitat

A bog is an area with saturated, organic-rich soil that occurs where drainage is limited. A muskeg is a bog with scattered, stunted trees. Boggy areas in the Temperate Rainforest fit the latter and are appropriately called muskeg. The stunted tree of muskeg in Southeast Alaska is shore pine (p. 82), a tree that is not found in the forest.

Where the soil volume is filled with water there is no room for air. Oxygen enters the soil only slowly by diffusion through the water from the air above. Most decomposer microorganisms— bacteria and fungi—require oxygen. Consequently, microbial activity and decomposition of dead organic matter proceed very slowly in bogs. The result is slow nutrient release and the buildup of dead organic matter as peat. Alaskan muskeg stands have not had enough time since the last retreat of glacial ice to accumulate very deep deposits of peat like those of Ireland and Scotland, but they are headed in that direction.

Sitka black-tailed deer foraging in the muskeg. The trees are shore pines.

Some microorganisms can function, albeit slowly, in the absence of oxygen. The products of anaerobic (= without oxygen) microbial activity include organic acids, so muskeg soils are highly acidic. Plants of the muskeg get lots of light and plenty of water, but acid soil and slow nutrient release lead to extreme nutrient limitation of plant growth. The plants that grow in muskeg must be tolerant of these conditions but they grow slowly and are easily outcompeted by other plants where nutrients are more available. Consequently, most plants of the muskeg are not found in forest or meadows, and there is an abrupt and radical change in species composition as one passes from forest into muskeg. However, plants of the muskeg are often found disjunctly in alpine and arctic tundra, where conditions are similar: acid soils that are rich in organic matter and limited in nutrient availability.

Notable among the muskeg plants are two species of sundews (pp. 132-133). These are insectivorous plants that supplement their nutrient supply by capturing and digesting small flies using sticky glands on their leaves. Sphagnum moss (p. 63) is particularly abundant in muskeg. Its slowly decomposing remains make up a large part of the accumulating peat.

Muskeg covers more than 10 percent of Southeast Alaska. It is not restricted to low points on the landscape. It can occur at all elevations, sometimes well up on the mountains, and on sites with noticeable slope. In fact, it can be a bit difficult to say just why muskeg occurs where it does.

Within an area of muskeg, and especially around the margin, we often find dead snags of larger trees. They were formerly able to grow where large trees can no longer flourish. This indicates that boggy conditions are becoming more severe and areas of muskeg are expanding; that is, muskeg is encroaching on the surrounding forest. The bog condition must not result from underlying bedrock since that would not change over time. An alternative explanation is the accumulation of a chemical precipitate in the soil. If this process continues in the future, as seems likely, muskeg will come to occupy an even larger part of the landscape

Stepping onto the muskeg is like stepping onto a big, wet sponge. We discourage people from walking on muskeg because the vegetation mat is easily disturbed. In some places boardwalks have been constructed to provide visitor access to muskeg without damaging it. The Petersburg Creek Trail on Kupreanof Island, across Wrangell Narrows from Petersburg, provides access to a fine example of Alaskan muskeg along a boardwalk trail. There is another boardwalk trail through a small muskeg bog near the Alaska Raptor Rehabilitation Center in Sitka.

Oysterleaf and Beach Pea on the gravel of the upper beach of Fox Creek, Chichagof Island.

Beach (shoreline) habitats

Alaska has more shoreline than the sum of all of the contiguous states. Shorelines offer a rich set of habitats for plant growth. Since most landings, at least from small ships, occur on beaches visitors are quickly exposed to shoreline plants.

Where beaches are protected from the force of winter storms plant growth extends well below the high tide line and the intertidal area is alternately marine at high tide and terrestrial at low tide. Marine algae (seaweeds) grow interspersed with sea plantain (p. 161), and sea milkwort (p. 168) grows amid barnacle-covered rocks, its flowers even remaining open under the high tides.

Southeast Alaska has a huge tidal range; for example, the mean tidal range (mean high water to mean low water) in spring at Juneau is more than sixteen feet; the tides are even greater at the new and full moons. Where the beach gradient is low the intertidal zone is enormous; boaters had better be careful when they anchor their boat ashore, lest it float away on a rapidly rising tide or be stranded far from the water on a falling tide!

A coastal brown bear and her cub foraging in the coastal meadow habitat on the Katmai coast. (See page 32.)

Above the intertidal zone, there is a clear zonation with respect to substrate and to the amount of exposure to salt water that the plants can tolerate.   For instance, beach rye grass (p. 107) is always found on gravel in a band above the high tide line; beach pea (p. 147) and oysterleaf (p. 119) occur on gravel along the seaward edge of the beach rye zone.   Plants such as villous cinquefoil (p. 185) are found on rocky outcrops above the beach, and shore pine (p. 82), which is otherwise restricted to muskeg, can sometimes be found on top of such outcrops.

Shootingstars and Alaska lupines adorn a Coastal Meadow at Kelp Bay on Baranof Island.

Coastal meadow habitat

On flat surfaces close to sea level and around shallow lakes, we find a wet meadow community. Here soils are wet but not as anaerobic (lacking in oxygen) as in muskeg. The meadow plant community is dominated by grasses, sedges, and a diversity of herbaceous (non-woody) flowering plants. The vegetation can be dense, productive, and very beautiful with bright showy flowers of all colors. These are wonderful places to scan for brown bears foraging on sedges and other meadow plants in spring and early summer.

Alpine habitat on Mount Roberts, above Juneau, near the end of June.

Alpine habitat

Alpine habitats are beyond the scope of this book. Most visitors do not have (or make) the opportunity to explore the alpine zone. That is a pity because the land above the tree line is rich in beautiful and interesting flowering plants. I can only suggest that visitors to Juneau ride the convenient tramway up Mount Roberts and take advantage of easy walking trails into the alpine vegetation for a rewarding experience.

Biogeography

Biogeography is the study of the geographic distribution of organisms. In studying biogeography we begin by cataloging the diversity of organisms in some area of interest. While this book makes no claims to be a complete catalog, it is a starting point, a list of the most common and familiar plants of Coastal Alaska. The next step in biogeography is to search for patterns in the data set. The final step is to propose (or hypothesize) reasons for the patterns that are observed, and to search for ways to test the hypotheses.

Coastal Alaska is an interesting place for such an analysis because the landscape and the communities are new. Glaciers have covered most of the land during the recurrent glacial episodes of the Pleistocene ice ages. Until the last retreat of the ice some 14,000 to 12,000 years ago glaciers occupied most of the southern third or so of Alaska, up to the mountains of the Alaska Range. Only a few years ago I would have written "All of the land ...", but recent evidence indicates that some coastal areas must have been ice-free, allowing plants and animals to live in glacial refugia, and quite possibly helping to support human populations as they migrated southward following the coastline. But that is another story.

We see evidence of glaciation all around us. The waterways of coastal Alaska are fjords—glacially carved valleys now flooded by the sea. Some of them are open at both ends, allowing thru transit by ships in calm, protected waters. Other fjords end in tidewater glaciers that drop ice into the sea, and in yet others the ice has retreated onto land or disappeared entirely, leaving behind coastal meadows where land meets the sea. The steep walls of the glacial valleys and fjords are polished by the passage of ice and etched by rocks carried along by the glaciers. Hanging valleys—U-shaped with steep sides—show us where tributary glaciers once joined the main valley glacier. Waterfalls too numerous to count plunge down the vertical faces of the valleys, bringing water from melting snow early in the season and from the frequent rains of summer. Peaks of less than a few thousand feet have been rounded by the ice. There can be no question that ice has shaped this landscape.

In contrast, most of Alaska north of the Alaska Range was not glaciated, not because it was warmer there, but because cold

The action of glaciers has resulted in characteristic landscape features: U-shaped hanging valleys, near-vertical rock walls, and unnumerable waterfalls, as seen here along the beautiful fjord of Tracy Arm, which cuts into mainland Alaska near Juneau.

air holds less moisture to fall as snow and accumulate as ice. Unglaciated Alaska was continuous across the Bering Platform, now under a shallow ocean but then exposed to include a large swath of present-day Asia.

We give the name Beringia to the unglaciated parts of Alaska and adjacent Asia. There is dispute in detail but agreement in general that Beringia supported a tundra-like plant assemblage. There were no trees but there was an abundance of shrubs, herbs, grasses and sedges. They left evidence as pollen deposits in the peat of ancient lake bottoms.

Some paleontologists argue convincingly that it must have been a productive community to support the populations of large grazing mammals—mammoths, bison, horses, saiga antelope, caribou, and more—that lived there. We find an abundance of their bones in those same peat deposits as these are exposed by riverbank erosion and by placer mining for gold.

Norio Matsumoto

The retreat of the glaciers has left behind a maze of waterways that forms the "marine highway" system of Southeast Alaska.

The plants that colonized Coastal Alaska as the glacial ice retreated may have come from at least three sources: (1) unglaciated lands south of the continental glaciers—the plants may have followed the glaciers as they retreated northward. (2) unglaciated Beringia—the plants may have moved southward as new land was exposed. (3) glacial refugia—plant populations may have spread from ice-free patches within a generally glaciated landscape.

I suspect that plant communities in any glacial refugia (3) would be very similar to the communities of unglaciated Beringia (2). I have not been able to think of a clever way to distinguish between these hypotheses. Glacial refugia would surely have been small and lower in diversity than Beringia, but otherwise similar. The scarce occurrence of endemic species—plants that occur ONLY in coastal Alaska—supports this view.

The plant species of the Temperate Forest are, to a large extent, of North American origin. None of the tree species of Coastal

Alaska occur naturally in Asia. The same can be said for a majority of the shrub and herb species of the forest. This argues, I think, for hypothesis 1: as the glaciers retreated, the suite of species that we now find in coastal Alaskan forest came from the south and east, from the unglaciated parts of North America.

The muskeg bog habitat is very different. It is full of plants that do not occur in the adjacent forest but are widely distributed in similar habitats all around the northern part of the globe. Many of the plant species were described by the Swedish Botanist Carl von Linné, or Carolus Linnaeus, in the early 1700s, but Linnaeus never visited Alaska. He described these species from Lapland.

Bogs in Lapland and Alaska have many of the same species, but forests in Lapland and Alaska have different species. The same can be said of forests and bogs in Alaska and Eastern Asia, and it can be said for insects as well as plants. Further, many of the plants of the bogs are also found in alpine tundra above the tree line, and in Arctic tundra far to the north beyond the limit of tree distribution. So the muskeg bog habitat was most likely not colonized by hypothesis 1, by plants moving northward as glaciers retreated, but by some combination of hypotheses 2 and 3. I suspect that hypothesis 2 was the more important. Unglaciated Beringia was a refuge for plants and insects that are now found in tundra and bog communities around the circumpolar north, but these species have not invaded the forests.

Exploring a waterway at Tekatz Bay, Baranof Island.

Plant Identification

Fungi

Fungi are not plants; they belong to another Kingdom of life altogether. Fungi of different species play different roles in the ecosystem. Some exist with an algal partner as part of the lichen symbiosis. Some are plant parasites. Yet others are decomposers that break down dead organic matter; these are very important in the recycling of nutrients.

Decomposer fungi may be free-living, but many live in an intimate and mutualistic relationship with the roots of higher plants, called a mycorrhizal (fungus-root) association. The fungus takes up nutrients that are used by the plant; the plant provides energy in the form of sugar. Most of the fungus consists of very, very fine filaments called hyphae that spread throughout the decomposing material, secreting enzymes that break it down. What we see and classify (and sometimes eat) are the reproductive structures (= fruiting bodies) of the fungi.

Important note: Please do not assume that a mushroom is safe to eat based on information in this guide. Many toxic species resemble edible species. Even experts make mistakes. When there is ANY doubt or possibility of misidentification, err on the side of caution. Wild mushrooms are particularly risky when they are eaten with alcohol. Eating wild mushrooms is a great experience, but you should do so only under the guidance of someone with whom you are willing to trust your life … because you will be.

Fly Amanita
Fly Agaric

Amanita muscaria

This is Alaska's most distinctive and <u>most toxic</u> mushroom. It is round, orange to scarlet, and covered with white warty structures when young. In a few days it opens to a flat platform with white gills and spores on the underside, and the red color may fade to yellow-orange. It is hallucinogenic in small doses but the difference between a small dose and a fatal dose is small. Trying it will put your life at risk, so don't do it.

Beach
Edge
Forest
Meadow
Muskeg

Shelf Fungus
Artist's Conk

Ganoderma applanatum

This fungus is the major decomposer of dying and dead trees, both conifers and hardwoods. The shelf is hard and perennial, growing a new layer each year. The upper surface is brown; the lower surface is white and consists of innumerable pores, not gills as in the more familiar fungi. When the white lower surface is scratched a brown line remains.

| Beach |
| Edge |
| Forest |
| Meadow |
| Muskeg |

Sulfur Shelf
Chicken-of-the-Woods

Laetiporus sulphureus

This is another polypore fungus with pores on
the lower surface rather than gills. It forms
large clusters of overlapping shelves on dead
wood. They are bright orange above and paler
yellow on the underside. Many people find it
edible, especially when young. A small percent-
age of people suffer an adverse reaction, so it
should be tried in small amounts.

Beach
Edge
Forest
Meadow
Muskeg

Stephen Handley

Bird's Nest Fungus

Cyathus species

These very small (smaller than a dime) open cups show "splash-cup" spore dispersal. Most commonly bird's nest fungi are on fallen pieces of bark and small dead twigs on the forest floor.

Beach
Edge
Forest
Meadow
Muskeg

Golden Jelly Cone

Heterotextus alpinus
(or Guepiniopsis alpina)

This fungus looks like small blobs of golden
jelly, commonly arrayed along dead twigs
lying on the ground. They can appear very
early in the season, and are sometimes called
snow fungi. They are decomposers of wood.

Beach
Edge
Forest
Meadow
Muskeg

Lichens

These are not plants either, but a mutualistic partnership (symbiosis = "living together") of an alga and a fungus.

The algal cells are contained within the fungus. The fungus provides structure and takes up water and nutrients; the algae are photosynthetic and contribute sugar (energy) to the relationship.

The algal component of some lichens is nitrogen-fixing; it takes gaseous nitrogen (N_2) from the air and incorporates it into protein. When the lichen falls and decomposes, this nitrogen enters the forest ecosystem as NO_3 that can be used by plants in their own growth. Higher plants (flowering plants) cannot fix nitrogen, although some such as alder have nitrogen-fixing bacteria associated with their roots.

Because of their role in nutrient dynamics, nitrogen-fixing lichens are very important in the economy of the forest.

A recent checklist to the lichens of Alaska (Feuerer 2008) lists 727 species, 67 in the genus *Cladonia* alone. Often, related species cannot be told apart without a portable chemistry laboratory, so identification to genus is all that we can hope for in the field.

Lung Lichen
Lungwort

Lobaria pulmonaria

This large, leafy lichen is pale gray-green above and white below. It lives on branches high in the forest canopy. We usually see it on the ground after it has fallen. The algal component of this lichen is a Cyanobacterium (blue-green alga.) Lungwort is the most important nitrogen-fixing lichen of the forest.

Beach
Edge
Forest
Meadow
Muskeg

Cabbage Lungwort

Lobaria linita

This species is similar to lungwort (p. 45),
but it tends to grow on the ground and bases
of trees (seen here on the trunk of red alder)
rather than on high branches of conifers. It is
bright grass-green when wet.

Beach
Edge
Forest
Meadow
Muskeg

Frog's Pelt

Peltigera neopolydactyla

This large, leafy lichen grows loosely appressed to rocks, logs, or moss. It is olive-green to bluish-gray above, with brownish fruiting bodies that are on erect, narrow lobes along the thallus margins.

Beach
Edge
Forest
Meadow
Muskeg

Old Man's Beard
Methuselah's Beard

Usnea longissima

This large, hanging, hair-like epiphytic lichen commonly grows on conifers. It has a long unbranched central core and short lateral branchlets. It is very sensitive to pollution and is disappearing in Europe.

Beach
Edge
Forest
Meadow
Muskeg

Witch's Hair

Alectoria sarmentosa

This is another epiphytic, hanging, hair lichen. From a distance it resembles old man's
beard, but it is <u>intricately branched</u> in a net-
like fashion. It is an important winter food
for Sitka black-tailed deer.

Beach
Edge
Forest
Meadow
Muskeg

Speckled Horsehair

Bryoria fuscescens

Here is yet another hanging hair lichen. This
one is pale to dark brown. It occurs on conifers in open forests especially on shore pine
in muskegs.

Beach
Edge
Forest
Meadow
Muskeg

Gray Horsehair Lichen

Bryoria capillaris

This epiphytic lichen varies from pale gray
to gray-green. It is found growing on conifer
branches in damp spots such as in waterfall
mist.

Beach
Edge
Forest
Meadow
Muskeg

Cladonia

Cladonia species

Beach
Edge
Forest
Meadow
Muskeg

There are many species of *Cladonia*, differing in details of form and chemistry. You need a portable chemistry kit for a complete identification. The erect stalks look like golf tees, and are often covered with a granular powdery substance.

The cup may be red-tipped (e.g. Toy Soldiers or British Soldiers - *C. bellidiflora.*)

Reindeer Lichens

(sometimes called Reindeer Moss, but it is
most definitely <u>not</u> a moss)

Cladina species

These are fruticose lichens that are intricately
branched, usually white to pale yellow. They
are crisp when dry, soft when damp.

Beach
Edge
Forest
Meadow
Muskeg

Foam Lichen

Stereocaulon species

These are usually gray and very granular in appearance. They may look a bit like cauliflower ... or maybe not. They are usually found on the forest floor.

Beach
Edge
Forest
Meadow
Muskeg

Shield Lichens

Parmelia species

These are the most abundant foliose lichens on deciduous trees. The texture is a combination of ridges and depressions, like hammered metal. *P. sulcata* is probably our most common foliose lichen.

Emily Mount

Beach
Edge
Forest
Meadow
Muskeg

Starburst Lichens

Parmeliopsis species

These are closely appressed foliose lichens on weathered old bark and wood, especially conifers. They have very narrow radiating lobes. The most common species, *P. hyperopta*, is gray. If it is green it is *P. ambigua*.

Beach
Edge
Forest
Meadow
Muskeg

Sunburst Lichens

Xanthoria candelaria

This bright yellow or orange lichen forms
encrusting growth on rock or wood. Many
Xanthoria species are found on animal-fertil-
ized spots like rocks below bird perches or
bird breeding colonies.

Beach
Edge
Forest
Meadow
Muskeg

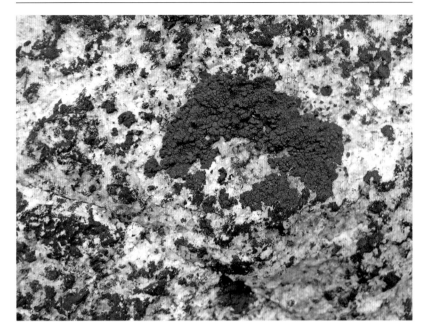

Sea Tar

Verrucaria maura

This lichen forms a conspicuous black band on the rocks just above the high tide line. It can be a continuous stripe about two feet high, or discrete patches as seen here. It looks a bit like the residue of on oil spill ... but it isn't.

Beach
Edge
Forest
Meadow
Muskeg

BRYOPSIDA

The Mosses

These are non-vascular plants, lacking an internal transport system (conducting tissue, or "plumbing"). For this reason, mosses can never become very tall. They usually form low-growing mats on the forest floor and on the trunks and branches of trees. An abundance of moss on the tree trunks and branches (and not just on the north-facing side) is one of the defining characteristics of the Temperate Rain Forest.

Step Moss

Hylocomium splendens

This is one of the most abundant mosses of the forest. The fern-like leaves are in step-like annual increments, all on the same side of the stem. You can find six or more increments on a single plant, with the new growth on the top and dead, decomposing tissue at the base. It is often found growing around the bases of large trees in Old-Growth Forest.

| Beach |
| Edge |
| Forest |
| Meadow |
| Muskeg |

Big Red Stem
Feather Moss

Pleurozium schreberi

It is olive-green in color, forming intertwined colonies on the ground and on fallen logs and stumps. It branches on either side of the stem. The branches are red. Recent research has shown the *Pleurozium* is an important nitrogen-fixing organism due to symbiotic blue-green algae (*Nostoc*) that convert atmospheric nitrogen, N_2, to nitrate, NO_3. When the moss decomposes the nitrate is released and can be used by other plants.

Beach
Edge
Forest
Meadow
Muskeg

Haircap Moss
Starburst Moss

Polytrichum species

They look like little green starbursts, often
with a wiry sporophyte (reproductive stalk)
coming out of the top. These are very abundant in the Old-Growth Forest.

Beach
Edge
Forest
Meadow
Muskeg

Large Leafy Moss

Rhizomnium glabrescens

The widely spreading upper leaves are oval, about twice as long as wide, and are arranged like small green flowers, each with a dark spot in the center. It is common on decomposing logs and other moist organic substrate of Old-Growth Forests.

Beach
Edge
Forest
Meadow
Muskeg

Sphagnum Moss

Sphagnum species

This is a defining plant of acid bogs and muskeg, but *Sphagnum* species also occur in very
wet forests. The leaves are in shaggy rosettes,
often densely packed. *Sphagnum* mats may
be reddish to rich burgundy in color.

Sphagnum can hold an enormous amount of
water. Native people used it for baby diapers,
dressing wounds, and for other forms of per-
sonal hygiene.

Beach
Edge
Forest
Meadow
Muskeg

MARCHANTIOPHYTA

Liverworts

These are low-growing, non-vascular plants that are related to mosses.

Snake Liverwort

Conocephalum conicum

Beach
Edge
Forest
Meadow
Muskeg

This large liverwort is flat and ribbon-like, somewhat branched, and folded longitudinally to appear trough-like. The upper surface is divided into hexagonal sections, each with a dark pore in the center. It grows in moist places, often on rocks or inorganic soil, but here it was growing on a fallen red alder.

LYCOPODIACEAE

The Club Mosses

These plants do have vascular (conducting) tissue but they lack flowers. They are the oldest and most primitive of the vascular plants. They were dominant plants during the Mesozoic Era—the Age of the Dinosaurs—and were eaten by herbivorous dinosaurs before the higher, flowering plants had evolved.

Stiff Clubmoss

Lycopodium annotinum

This one has a trailing stem with little branching. The erect leafy stems, often paired, are covered with spreading leaves. The spore-producing structures are sessile (= unstalked) atop the leafy stems. It occurs in drier forests and meadows.

Beach
Edge
Forest
Meadow
Muskeg

Running Clubmoss

Lycopodium clavatum

It has a horizontal stem that is long, creeping, and extensively branched. The ascending branches are much forked, with leaves
lying flat to the stems. Spores are produced
in 1-3 yellowish cylindrical cones at the ends
of long, erect stalks. It is found on the forest
floor.

Beach
Edge
Forest
Meadow
Muskeg

Fir Clubmoss

Lycopodium (= Huperzia) selago

This clubmoss has erect stems that are generally 2 to 4 inches long, and dichotomously
branched (in pairs), the branches of each pair
of equal length. The lance-shaped leaves are
in eight ranks around the stem. There are
often constrictions (shorter leaves) that delin-
eate annual growth increments. This is a very
widely distributed plant, found throughout
Alaska and widely around the globe.

Beach
Edge
Forest
Meadow
Muskeg

EQUISETACEAE

The Horsetails

This is another group of primitive vascular plants that lack flowers. They are related to the clubmosses.

Field Horsetail

Equisetum arvense

Beach
Edge
Forest
Meadow
Muskeg

It has erect, pale-green, plumose stems. The separate fertile stems lack chlorophyll; they appear in spring. It is one of the planet's most widely distributed plants.

POLYPODIACEAE

The Ferns

This is yet another group of non-flowering vascular plants. They reproduce by spores, which are commonly found in structures called sori (singular sorus) on the underside of the leaflets. The arrangement of the sori is a useful trait in identification.

Maidenhair Spleenwort

Asplenium trichomanes

This small and simple fern grows in bunches right out of vertical walls of limestone cliffs above the sea. The yellow-green leaflets are evergreen, leathery and nearly opposite. The rachis (the main axis of the frond, between the leaflets) is dark.

Beach
Edge
Forest
Meadow
Muskeg

Green Spleenwort

Asplenium viride

This small spleenwort is densely tufted from
short rhizomes. The oval leaflets are opposite
at the base of the frond, becoming alternate
distally (toward the tip.) The rachis of the
frond is green. It is found growing on wet
rocky places, especially on limestone.

Beach
Edge
Forest
Meadow
Muskeg

Oak Fern

Gymnocarpium dryopteris

This very common small fern of the forest has tripartite leaves forming a terminal and two lateral triangles; each of these is then further dissected. Look for the dark petiole that divides into three.

Beach
Edge
Forest
Meadow
Muskeg

Northern Beech-fern

Thelypteris phegopteris

This is a fern of openings and forest edges. It has a single frond, with a petiole that is longer than the blade. The lowermost pinnae are the largest, and point back toward the rachis.

Beach
Edge
Forest
Meadow
Muskeg

Deer Fern

Blechnum spicant

It has two types of fronds. The vegetative
fronds are evergreen, forming a rosette near
the ground. The fertile fronds appear in
summer. They are more open (with narrow pinnae) and erect, ascending above the
vegetative fronds. As the name indicates, the
overwintering vegetative fronds are eaten by
deer.

Beach
Edge
Forest
Meadow
Muskeg

Lady Fern

Athyrium felix-femina

This common fern has erect stalks spreading
from the base. The leaves are two to three
times pinnate, and widest in the center, taper-
ing toward both ends. The stipes at the base
of the fronds are short and scaly. The fronds
grow anew each season, opoening from
prominent fiddleheads (left).

Beach
Edge
Forest
Meadow
Muskeg

Licorice Fern

Polypodium glycyrrhiza

This small to medium fern often grows
on logs, over rocks, and on the trunk and
branches of deciduous trees, but not on the
ground. The leaves are once-pinnate, the
leaflets offset. The name comes from the rhizome, which contain the same chemical that
gives licorice its flavor.

Beach
Edge
Forest
Meadow
Muskeg

Maidenhair Fern

Adiantum pedatum

The stem, radiating out into the fronds, is
black and hairless. There are 10-12 fronds
that radiate fan-like. They are largest in the
center and smaller at the outer edges of the
fan. It occurs in wet areas, on rock cliffs, and
along stream banks.

Beach
Edge
Forest
Meadow
Muskeg

A kayak is a fine way to enjoy the serenity of the coastal Temperate Rainforest.

(left) **Tracy Arm-Fords Terror Wilderness**

(below) **Hanus Bay, Baranof Island**

Gymnospermae

Gymnosperms are the first seed-bearing plants in the fossil record, appearing some 350 million years ago. The seeds develop without protection of an ovary. ("Gymnosperm" means "naked seed".) The cone-bearing plants (conifers) are, by far, the most abundant and diverse of the living gymnosperms.

PINACEAE
The Pine Family

The leaves are needle-like.

Sitka Spruce

Picea sitchensis

Look for the scaly bark. The needles extend all around the branches and are sharp to the touch.

Sitka spruce is the largest of all spruces, exceeding eight feet in diameter and 240 feet in height. The largest trees are found near salmon spawning streams where they receive an annual input of nutrients from salmon carcasses. Sitka spruce is a relatively fast growing tree that is characteristic of successional stands, forest edges, and light gaps. In the first picture (left), the lighter green is the new growth in the characteristic pattern of two lateral and a terminal bud.

In some years spruce make a massive investment in reproduction, synchronized across the population, and the branches are heavily laden with cones. In other years cone production is low to nil. Red squirrels feed on seeds in the cones of spruce. They store cones below ground and bring them to the surface to eat, leaving piles of cone scales and the de-scaled cores of cones, not unlike little corn cobs. These "middens" are a conspicuous feature of spruce forest. Storage of cones serves to even out the large year-to-year variation in production of cones. (See photo, page 19.)

Beach
Edge
Forest
Meadow
Muskeg

Western Hemlock

Tsuga heterophylla

From a distance, look for the drooping top of the tree. The branches form flat sprays. The needles, in two ranks on either side of the branches, are soft to the touch. The cones are small but numerous. The bark is furrowed, not scaly. It is a smaller tree than Sitka spruce, not that six feet in diameter and 200 feet in height is all that small. Hemlock is a long-lived, slow-growing tree of old-growth forests. It often germinates on nurse logs and grows in dim light, and thus it replaces spruce in forest succession. It is the most abundant tree of Old-Growth Forest in Southeast Alaska.

| Beach |
| Edge |
| Forest |
| Meadow |
| Muskeg |

Mountain Hemlock

Tsuga mertensiana

This tree is smaller tree than western hemlock and is often found around muskegs.
The needle arrangement is less orderly (not
in flat sprays) and the cones are larger than
the Western hemlock. It replaces Western
hemlock at higher elevations and becomes a
more important forest tree farther north, for
example around Cook Inlet.

Beach
Edge
Forest
Meadow
Muskeg

Shore Pine

Pinus contorta var. *contorta*

This is the most common tree of muskeg
bogs, where it is stunted and widely spaced.
It is also found along rocky shores. It seems
to require open conditions with lots of light
and is unable to compete in the forest. It has
the longest needles of any SE Alaskan conifer.
There are two needles per bundle. The cones
are persistent (they remain on the tree after
the seeds have been dispersed) and asymmetrical.

Beach
Edge
Forest
Meadow
Muskeg

CUPRESSACEAE
The Cypress Family

The leaves are scale-like, not needle-like.

Yellow Cedar
Alaska Cedar

Chamaecyparis nootkatensis

The branches are spreading and drooping.
The foliage is in flat sprays; the scale-like
leaves are yellow-green. The cones are small,
hard, and nearly round. Alaska cedar grows
as a tree in forest, but a shrub in muskegs. In
places there has been heavy mortality of Alaska cedar, leaving dead snags standing in the
forest. This phenomenon, known as yellow
cedar decline, has been going on since about
1880. Recent research relates yellow cedar
death to warmer winter weather, which leads
to diminished snow cover, which (somewhat
paradoxically) increases the likelihood that
roots will suffer from freezing during the occasional cold spells.

Beach
Edge
Forest
Meadow
Muskeg

Western Red Cedar

Thuja plicata

Beach
Edge
Forest
Meadow
Muskeg

This massive tree reaches over 200 ft (60 m) with a huge trunk. The bark is fibrous, gray to reddish. The branches droop then sweep upward, J-shaped. The small cones, concentrated near the tips of the branches, have few (8-12) scales. This is a most important tree to Native People of the Pacific Northwest, providing food, clothing and wood planks for building their long-houses and canoes. In Alaska, it reaches north only to the vicinity of Petersburg; it does not occur on the "ABC Islands" of Admiralty, Baranof and Chichagof.

Juniper

Juniperus communis

This is a shrub of alpine and muskeg habitats.
It has sharp-tipped, awl-shaped needles. The
cones are berry-like, first green, then becoming blue. Juniper berries are used to flavor
gin.

Beach
Edge
Forest
Meadow
Muskeg

Angiospermae

These are the true flowering plants. The Angiosperms are the most recent, most advanced, and most successful of the seed-bearing plants. The seeds develop within the protection of a carpel, which matures into the fruit.

There are two main branches of the Angiospermae: the **Monocotledonae**, treated in this section, and the **Dicotyledonae**, considered in the next section. Monoctotyledons have in common parallel leaf veination, and flowering parts in threes and sixes. They draw their name from the fact that the very young seedling has only one seed leaf.

ARACEAE
The Arum Family

Skunk Cabbage

Lysichiton americanum

The huge leaves are shiny and rubbery. It
occurs in very wet places in the forest, meadows, and bogs. The flowers appear very early
in spring, before the leaves emerge. The tiny
flowers are arranged on an erect fleshy spike
(spathe) that is partially enclosed by a bright
yellow bract (spadix.) Skunk cabbage is pollinated by small beetles (*Pelecomalius testaceum:*
Staphylinidae), and they may be very abundant
on the spathe. In spring deer often bite off the
spathes and the tips of the emerging leaves,
and brown bears dig up the fleshy roots. Crys-
tals of calcium oxalate make the leaves inedible
for people. Indian people used the large leaves
as wrapping paper.

Beach
Edge
Forest
Meadow
Muskeg

CYPERACEAE
The Sedges

They are grass-like, but "sedges have edges"; that is, the leaf bases form a triangle in cross-section. Grasses, in contrast, are round at the base.

Lyngby's Sedge

Carex lyngbyaei

Beach
Edge
Forest
Meadow
Muskeg

This is the dominant sedge of coastal meadows and tidal marshes. The inflorescence is made up of plump green sacs subtended by brown scales. The whole plant is rich in protein. The roots and rhizomes are an important spring food for bears, geese, and swans.

Mike Greenfelder

Cotton Grass
Arctic Cotton

Eriophorum angustifolium

Grass-like, but it is actually a sedge. It has
two to eight cottony tufts in a loose, drooping terminal cluster. This plant is found in
saturated sites, often with standing water.

| Beach |
| Edge |
| Forest |
| Meadow |
| Muskeg |

Tufted Clubrush

Trichophorum cespitosum
(=Scirpus cespitosus)

[Note: the *Flora of North America* (1993+) and other sources have corrected the common misrepresentation of Linnaeus' "cespitosa", as "caes…" See also *Vaccinium cespitosum*, p. 145.] "Cespitose" means tufted or densely clustered. This one consists of bunches of green, reed-like stems. The stems have ridges and intervening troughs running the length of the stem. You can find leaf sheaths at the bases of the stems. The flowers are solitary and sit on the tips of the stems. It is common in muskegs.

Beach
Edge
Forest
Meadow
Muskeg

IRIDACEAE
The Iris Family

Blue Flag Iris

Iris setosa

This is a most unmistakable and beautiful
plant. The leaves are linear and laterally
compressed. The very large, showy flowers
have three enormous blue and white petaloid (= petal-like) sepals and three smaller
blue petals. Both the roots and the seeds are
poisonous.

Beach
Edge
Forest
Meadow
Muskeg

JUNCAGINACEAE
The Arrowgrass Family

Sea Arrowgrass

Triglochin maritima

Despite the name, this is not a grass but part
of a separate family that consists of only
about 25 or so species. This highly tufted
plant grows on intertidal flats where it is an
important, nutritious food for migrating
geese.

Beach
Edge
Forest
Meadow
Muskeg

LILIACEAE
The Lily Family

Queen's Cup

Clintonia uniflora

The two to three basal leaves are elliptical, broadest nearer the tip, with prominent parallel veins. There is a single large white flower with six spreading petals on an erect stem. Later this becomes a single large blue berry, so the plant concentrates all its annual reproductive effort into a single progeny. It grows in the deep forest.

Beach
Edge
Forest
Meadow
Muskeg

Chocolate Lily
Northern Riceroot

Fritillaria camschatcensis

This plant has dark purple-brown flowers that are nodding. The bulb, like a wad of white rice, was an important source of carbohydrates for Native people. The foul odor of the flowers attests to their pollination by flies, and gives rise to another common name: "outhouse lily." It is an abundant plant of moist meadows.

| Beach |
| Edge |
| Forest |
| Meadow |
| Muskeg |

False Lily-of-the-Valley
Deerberry

Maianthemum dilatatum

This very abundant plant of the forest and
forest edges often forms a continuous carpet.
The leaves are heart-shaped, fairly large, and
conspicuously parallel-veined. It has many
small white flowers packed on an erect stalk
above the leaves. The berries are tan-colored,
spotted, becoming red when dry.

Beach
Edge
Forest
Meadow
Muskeg

Clasping Twisted Stalk
Watermelon Berry

Streptopus amplexifolius

The stems are branched, bending at each leaf node. The leaves are alternate, their bases surrounding (clasping) the stem. The spreading bell-shaped flowers are pale green, hanging below the leaves at each leaf axil on a kinked or abruptly twisted stalk. You do not see the flowers until you lift the stalk. The berries are watermelon-colored; they are juicy but not particularly flavorful.

| Beach |
| Edge |
| Forest |
| Meadow |
| Muskeg |

Rosy Twisted Stalk

Streptopus roseus

This is a smaller, <u>unbranched</u> version of the
clasping twisted stalk. The leaf bases meet
but do not clasp the stem. The flowers are
rose-colored, on curved (not kinked) stalks
hanging down from the leaf axils.

Beach
Edge
Forest
Meadow
Muskeg

False Hellebore
Corn Lily

Veratrum viride subsp *escholtzianum*

Beach
Edge
Forest
Meadow
Muskeg

This is a robust plant with an unbranched stem. The large leaves are conspicuously parallel-veined and accordion-pleated. Numerous small green flowers are densely packed in branched terminal clusters. The whole plant is deadly poisonous due to a nasty alkaloid called helleborine!

Sticky False Asphodel

Triantha (Tofieldia) glutinosa

This small lily occurs in muskeg bogs. The leaves are linear, rather iris-like. The flowers are white or greenish-white, occurring in dense terminal clusters on flowering stems that stick up above the leaves. The closely related species *Triantha pusilla* occurs in alpine tundra.

Beach
Edge
Forest
Meadow
Muskeg

ORCHIDACEAE
Yes, there really are orchids in the north; they are not only tropical.

Heart-leaved Twayblade

Listera cordata

This very small plant may be quite abundant in the moss of Old-Growth Forest, where it tolerates the low light of the forest floor.

It has two opposite, clasping, heart-shaped stem leaves ("twayblade" means "two leaves" in Old English.) A stalk with six to twelve tiny and delicate flowers appears in late-May and June. They are first green, then becoming purplish-brown. The lower petal is bifid (split.)

Each flower looks like a tiny faerie flying over the forest. You will need a hand lens to see them and a macro lens to photograph them, but it is well worth the effort.

Twayblades have a remarkable system of pollination in which packets of pollen are released explosively onto small flies.

Beach
Edge
Forest
Meadow
Muskeg

Emily Mount

Northwestern Twayblade

Listera caurina

This is similar to heart-leaved twayblade, and the two species often grow intermixed in the moss of the forest floor. The stem leaves are not heart-shaped, but rounded at the base. The flowers are pale green and the lower lip is not split as it is in *L. cordata*.

Beach
Edge
Forest
Meadow
Muskeg

Bette Lu Krause

Fairy Slipper
Calypso Orchid

Calypso bulbosa

Beach
Edge
Forest
Meadow
Muskeg

This is a rare but unmistakable, showy orchid that grows in dense forests, often near the beach on smaller islands. It has a single basal leaf growing from a bulb-like corm. The leaf soon withers, leaving an erect, hairless stem. Each stem bears a single large, fragrant, pink and purple orchid. It flowers in May and June. The plant is very sensitive and should not be disturbed. Picking a flower will kill the plant.

Coralroot

Corallorhiza maculata

This orchid is saprophytic (living from dead organic matter) or, more correctly, mycotrophic: a fungal association on its roots, called mycorrhizae, decomposes the dead organic matter. It lacks chlorophyll, and the whole plant is red-purple. It is found in Old-Growth Forests.

Beach
Edge
Forest
Meadow
Muskeg

White Bog-orchid

Platanthera (= Habenaria) dilatata

Beach
Edge
Forest
Meadow
Muskeg

This orchid has very fragrant white to green-ish-white flowers all around the stem, with progressively younger flowers up the stem. The leaves are sheathing (surrounding the stem), getting smaller up the stem. It occurs in wet meadows and muskegs.

Slender Bog-orchid
Rein Orchid

Platanthera (= Habenaria)
stricta (= P. saccata)

This is much like white bog orchid but the
flowers are green, often tinged with purple-
brown. The spur is inflated, sac-like.

Beach
Edge
Forest
Meadow
Muskeg

Emily Mount

Rattlesnake Plantain

Goodyera oblongifolia

This evergreen perennial has a basal rosette of oval leaves that are patterned with white, especially along the midrib. It has white to greenish flowers in a tall spike, mostly along one side. It grows in dark forests.

Beach
Edge
Forest
Meadow
Muskeg

POACEAE: The Grass Family

Beach Rye

Leymus (formerly *Elymus*) *mollis*

Some will say that it is a race of *L. arenarius* but the two species are distinct, with different numbers of chromosomes and distinct non-overlapping distributions.

This tall, coarse grass grows in dense stands on gravel above the high-tide line and just behind the beach crest. It reaches six feet in height. The leaves are blue-green. It is found on beaches all around the Northern Hemisphere. It is stripped very finely for use in Aleut basketry.

Beach
Edge
Forest
Meadow
Muskeg

SCHEUCHZERIACEAE:
The Scheuchzeria Family

There is only a single species in the family, as follows.

Scheuchzeria

Scheuchzeria palustris

This rush-like aquatic herb occurs in very wet bogs and lake margins. You will never notice it until its inflated fruits appear in clusters of 3 to12 late in the season; suddenly, it is conspicuous.

| Beach |
| Edge |
| Forest |
| Meadow |
| Muskeg |

The other main branch of the flowering plants (Angiospermae) is the **Dicotyledonae**. Plants of this large and diverse group tend to have net-like leaf veination, and flowering parts in something other than the threes and sixes of the Monocotyledoneae. The very young seedling has two seed leaves, but that is not a very useful characteristic for field identification.

ACERACEAE: The Maple Family

Douglas Maple

Acer glabrum

This small, extensively branched tree grows at the edge of the forest, often behind the beach line. The leaves are the typical maple shape—palmately-lobed and toothed. The yellow-green flowers appear in late May, in clusters among the leaves. The seed is the two-winged structure (samara) of familiar maples.

Beach
Edge
Forest
Meadow
Muskeg

APIACEAE
The Carrot or Parsley Family

The flowers are in a characteristic structure called an umbel, in which several to many flowering stems diverge radially from a common origin, like the spokes of an umbrella, to form a rounded or flat-topped inflorescence. The flowers are most commonly white.

Beach Lovage

Beach
Edge
Forest
Meadow
Muskeg

Ligusticum scoticum

The leaves consist of three thick, coarsely-toothed, hairless, and somewhat fleshy leaflets. It bears flat-topped umbels of very small white flowers.

Cow Parsnip
Indian Celery

Heracleum lanatum

This large, coarse plant is very common
throughout Southeast Alaska. The large
leaves are palmately lobed, coarsely toothed,
superficially like Devil's Club but more deeply
lobed. There is a huge terminal, flat-topped
umbel of white flowers; it is often covered
with flies. The young stalks and leaf stems
can be peeled and eaten. Older plants cause
a severe rash in some people, especially if the
skin is exposed to sunlight after contact.

Beach
Edge
Forest
Meadow
Muskeg

Seacoast Angelica
Sea-Watch

Angelica lucida

This is another coarse, stout perennial plant. The leaves are 2-3 times divided into threes; the leaflets are coarse-toothed and sharp-lobed. Where the leaf stem branches from the main stem there is an inflated sheath.

The white flowers are in compound umbels; that is, the flowering stem divides radially, and then divides again to end in discrete round clusters of small, white flowers.

You might also find the similar and related species Kneeling Angelica, *A. genuflexa*, in which the leaf stem is abruptly bent downward just beyond the first pair of leaflets.

Beach
Edge
Forest
Meadow
Muskeg

ARALIACEAE
The Ginsing Family

Devil's Club

Oplopanax horridus

If you learn to recognize only one plant of the forest, let it be this one. The name says it all. It has large maple-shaped leaves and nasty spines on the stems and on the veins of the underside of leaves. The spines fester painfully when embedded. It is a plant of light-gaps and forest edges. <u>Do not touch this plant!</u> Bears, however, are able to pull over the plant to eat the red berries. Native people have used devil's club for a wide variety of medicinal purposes, and devil's club balm can be purchased for whatever ails you.

Beach
Edge
Forest
Meadow
Muskeg

ASTERACEAE: The Composites
The Daisy Family

Douglas Aster

Symphyotrichum subspicatum
(= Aster subspicatus)
(= Aster douglasii)

Beach
Edge
Forest
Meadow
Muskeg

It is a plant of upper beaches, meadows, and open areas. The flower heads are solitary, the ray flowers blue-purple and strap-shaped; the disk flowers are yellow. Like other asters, it flowers late in the season.

Beach Groundsel

Senecio pseudoarnica

It occurs on sea beaches and tidal flats. The large leaves are densely-packed and woolly-hairy, especially on the lower surface. The large flowers appear late in the season: July-August. Both disk and ray flowers are yellow; the ray flowers are fairly long.

Beach
Edge
Forest
Meadow
Muskeg

Yarrow

Achillea millefolium

This strongly-scented herb has leaves that are very finely divided. The flowers are in flat-topped clusters, umbel-like, white or pink-purple. This is a very widely distributed plant, found all around the northern regions of the world.

Emily Mount

| Beach |
| Edge |
| Forest |
| Meadow |
| Muskeg |

BETULACEAE
The Birch Family

Red Alder

Alnus rubra

This tree forms groves along moist forest edges, stream banks, and revegetating clear-cuts. The bark is white. It will remind you of birch, but it is usually adorned with lichen and moss. The leaves are coarse-toothed. The "cones" are short-stalked. Alders are important nitrogen-fixers; bacteria in root nodules convert N_2 to NO_3, which is used by the alder to make protein. When alder leaves decompose the nitrogen is released and is taken up and used by other plants.

Beach
Edge
Forest
Meadow
Muskeg

Sitka Alder

Alnus sinuata
(= Alnus crispa ssp. sinuata)

This immensely common large shrub forms impenetrable thickets in forest openings and edges, clear-cuts, and in avalanche tracks. It very commonly grows between the beach and the forest. The leaves are doubly saw-toothed. The male catkins are large, showy, and rich in pollen. Female catkins are smaller, green, and above the male catkins. The fruit resemble small cones. The "cones" are long-stalked.

Beach
Edge
Forest
Meadow
Muskeg

Cones from previous years may persist on the bush long after the seeds are dispersed. You might find them in Alaskan gift shops electro-plated with gold and made into jewelry.

BORAGINACEAE
The Borage Family

Oysterleaf

Mertensia maritima

This low-growing plant grows in clumps
on gravel beaches just above the high tide
line. The fleshy blue-green foliage is reputed
to have the taste of oysters. It has sky-blue
flowers. It is widely distributed on beaches
around the circumpolar north.

Beach
Edge
Forest
Meadow
Muskeg

BRASSICACEAE
The Mustard Family

These have four petals and six stamens. The
stamens are often in a characteristic pattern
of four long and two short.

Little Western Bittercress

Cardamine oligosperma

This small (usually less than 25 cm, or 10
inches), erect herb is often found in the
Beach Rye zone of upper beaches, where it is
one of the first plants to flower in May. The
basal leaves are deeply divided into round
lobes; the lobes become larger distally with
the unpaired terminal lobe the largest. The
small white flowers occur in terminal clusters.

| Beach |
| Edge |
| Forest |
| Meadow |
| Muskeg |

CAMPANULACEAE
The Harebell or Bellflower Family

Common Harebell
Bluebells-of-Scotland

Campanula rotundifolia

This is a very showy plant with soft, blue
flowers, each on its own stem. The petals are
joined into a five-lobed bell. It is a plant of
open areas. Here it was growing on a limestone rock wall above the beach.

The flower seen above is infested with spider
mites.

Beach
Edge
Forest
Meadow
Muskeg

CAPRIFOLIACEAE
The Honeysuckle Family

Twinflower

Linnaea borealis

This trailing vine has leaves that are <u>opposite</u>, round, and sparsely-toothed. The erect flowering stalk, with a few opposite leaves, divides into a Y; each branch of the Y bears a single delicate pink, nodding, bell-shaped flower. It is the only plant to bear the name of the Swedish botanist and father of biological nomenclature (the naming of organisms) – Carl von Linne or, in Latin, Carolus Linnaeus.

| Beach |
| Edge |
| Forest |
| Meadow |
| Muskeg |

Highbush Cranberry

Viburnum edule

The leaves are opposite, and rounded at
the base with three pointed lobes directed
forward. White flowers, in clusters, yield
red berries that remain on the bush over the
winter or until eaten by birds. They make a
nice syrup.

Beach
Edge
Forest
Meadow
Muskeg

Red Elderberry

Sambucus racemosa

This large deciduous shrub has a distinctive unpleasant odor, especially when the leaves are crushed. The leaves are opposite and compound, each consisting of 5 to 7 leaflets. It has terminal clusters of many, cream-colored flowers. The small berries occur in red clusters. They are seedy but palatable <u>when cooked;</u> they are often made into syrup. The whole plant, including the fruit, contains cyanogenic glycosides and is toxic until cooked.

Beach
Edge
Forest
Meadow
Muskeg

CARYOPHYLLACEAE
The Pink Family

Beach Greens
Seabeach Sandwort

Honckenya peploides

This low-growing plant has stems that are densely covered with fleshy, pointed, somewhat succulent leaves. The flowers atop the leafy stems have prominent green sepals and smaller, white, spatula-shaped petals. It is common on gravel beaches near the high-tide line; it can even be covered by seawater at high tide.

Beach
Edge
Forest
Meadow
Muskeg

Field Chickweed

Cerastium arvense

This hairy little herb has linear or narrowly
lance-shaped leaves. The white flowers have
five deeply notched petals. It grows in well-
drained, open areas where it flowers over a
long period, May to July.

Beach
Edge
Forest
Meadow
Muskeg

CHENOPODIACEAE
The Goosefoot Family

Spearscale

Atriplex patula

This fleshy annual is another salt-tolerant plant of rocky beaches. It is usually branched and covered with a whitish scaly substance, looking as if rolled in cornmeal. The lower leaves are opposite, the upper are alternate, and quite variable in shape—linear to lanceolate to arrowhead-shaped. The flowers are in leafy axillary spikes, and lacking petals. The leaves and young stems can be used in salads.

Beach
Edge
Forest
Meadow
Muskeg

Sea Asparagus
Pickleweed

Salicornia depressa

It consists of very fleshy pale green, jointed stems growing in tight clusters in the inter-tidal zone where it is regularly covered by the tide. The tiny flowers appear late in the season; they are in groups of three, lacking petals. The whole plant is edible, tasting like salty pickles.

It is included in *Salicornia virginica* by earlier authors.

Beach
Edge
Forest
Meadow
Muskeg

CORNACEAE
The Dogwood
Family

Red-Osier Dogwood

Cornus (= Swida)
stolonifera (= C. sericea)

This is a large shrub to small tree. The lower
branches may root where they touch the
ground. The twigs are dark red. The leaves
are deciduous, opposite, with hairy petioles.
The white flowers are crowded into clusters at
the ends of the branches. Each flower gives
rise to a single white berry (sometimes with a
blue cast). It is found in moist soil in clear-
ings in the forest and along forest edges at
low elevations.

Beach
Edge
Forest
Meadow
Muskeg

Bog Bunchberry
Swedish Bunchberry

Cornus suecica
(= Chamaepericlymenum suecicum)
(or *C. suecica x canadensis*—a hybrid swarm showing a mixture of the characters of the two species and found in muskeg habitats)

This is a more erect form than dwarf dogwood with three pairs of stem leaves. The leaves are deciduous, turning red in fall. They are more boat-shaped – that is keeled and pointed at the tip, and the berries are redder than those of *canadensis*. It is found in the muskeg habitat.

Beach
Edge
Forest
Meadow
Muskeg

Dwarf Dogwood
Canadian Bunchberry

Cornus canadensis
(=Chamaepericlymenum canadense)

Low-growing. It has two very small, opposite
stem leaves plus whorls of four (on non-flowering stems) or six (on flowering stems) larger
leaves. What looks like a flower is actually
an inflorescence of tiny purple flowers subtended by four white petaloid bracts. These
are modified leaves that serve the function
of petals. Each flower, if pollinated, forms a
red-orange berry.

The berries are rather mealy and not attractive
to humans, but they are eaten by birds. The
evergreen leaves are an important winter food
for deer.

Beach
Edge
Forest
Meadow
Muskeg

DROSERACEAE
The Sundew Family

These are insectivorous plants. They thrive in
bogs where nutrients are in short supply.

Round-leaved Sundew

Drosera rotundifolia

This very small plant grows in the moss of
wet bogs and muskeg. The entire plant is red.
The round leaves are covered with gland-
tipped hairs that capture and digest insects. It
flowers in July, with 3 to 10 small white flowers arrayed along one side of a long, delicate
stem. It is usually associated with *Sphagnum*.

| Beach |
| Edge |
| Forest |
| Meadow |
| Muskeg |

Great Sundew

Drosera anglica

This is similar to round-leaved sundew, but
the leaves are erect and more linear. It grows
in ephemeral or intermittent ponds, where it
forms distinct clumps. It is much less common than *D. rotundifolia.*

Beach
Edge
Forest
Meadow
Muskeg

EMPETRACEAE
The Crowberry Family

Crowberry

Empetrum nigrum

This low, much-branched, evergreen sub-
shrub reaches only 20 cm (8 inches) or
so. The leaves are small, linear, in crowded
whorls around the erect woody stems. The
flowers are inconspicuous. The fruits are
purple-black, berry-like, tasty but seedy. They
are made into liquor in Scandinavia, but are
scarcely used here (except by bears.)

Beach
Edge
Forest
Meadow
Muskeg

ERICACEAE
The Heath Family

Bog Rosemary

Andromeda polifolia

This small plant of muskegs has dark-green, evergreen leaves. They are nearly linear and oriented vertically with the margins rolled under. The pink hanging-urn flowers appear in May and the first half of June. When it is not in flower it can be hard to see.

| Beach |
| Edge |
| Forest |
| Meadow |
| Muskeg |

Bog Laurel

Kalmia polifolia

Beach
Edge
Forest
Meadow
Muskeg

The flowers are rose-pink, saucer-shaped, in clusters atop the plant. It flowers early in the season and is much less conspicuous after flowering. The narrow leaves are opposite, evergreen, rolled under at the margins, and white-pubescent below. The leaves are not as narrow as those of Bog Rosemary.

Bearberry
Kinnikinnick

Arctostaphylos uva-ursi

This is a mat-forming subshrub. The ever-green leaves are light green, leathery, and simple along the margin. The white to pink urn-shaped flowers are clustered at the ends of the twigs. The berries are red and seedy. Bearberry occurs on dry, recently deglaciated slopes, on dry rocky bluffs along the coast, and in the alpine zone.

Beach
Edge
Forest
Meadow
Muskeg

Labrador Tea

Ledum groenlandicum

Beach
Edge
Forest
Meadow
Muskeg

This is a sparsely leaved evergreen sub-shrub. The leathery leaves are in tufts at the ends of branches. They are dark olive-green above, with orange felty pubescence on the underside. It has a globose head of white flowers in June/July. The dried leaves can be made into a tea, but I don't think you'll like it.

False Azalea
Fool's Huckleberry
Rusty Menziesia

Menziesia ferruginea

This is a common large shrub of the forest.
The leaves and flowers appear several weeks
later than other forest shrubs like blueberry
and huckleberry. The leaves are often blue-
green and occur in irregular whorls. The
urn-shaped flowers are salmon-colored. They
hang below the leaves, but after flowering
the flower stems turn upward so the fruits are
above the leaves.

The fruits are not edible; it would take quite a
fool to mistake them for edible huckleberries.

If you look very closely you will see a small fly
in the throat of this flower.

Beach
Edge
Forest
Meadow
Muskeg

Red Huckleberry

Vaccinium parvifolium

This is a medium-sized shrub that is often found growing on nurse logs. Look for the green and highly angled young stems. The oval leaves are in flat sprays, alternate, and often insect-munched. The inconspicuous flowers are single, hanging below the leaves, and yellow-green, sometimes with a hint of pink. The fruits are bright red.

Beach
Edge
Forest
Meadow
Muskeg

Lingonberry
Low-bush Cranberry

Vaccinium vitis-idaea

It is small and low-growing. The leaves are
evergreen, roundish, the edges somewhat
rolled under, the underside spotted with
brown glandular hairs. The flowers are in
clusters nodding on short stalks at the ends
of the twigs. The flowers are pink bells with
four short lobes. The stigma is long, extending beyond the bell. The red fruit is sour, but
makes a fine sauce for grouse or venison.

| Beach |
| Edge |
| Forest |
| Meadow |
| Muskeg |

Early Blueberry

Vaccinium ovalifolium

It is similar to *V. alaskaense*. The twigs are
strongly angled, and red-brownish. The pale
pink flowers appear before the leaves, in
April and May. They are longer than they are
broad. The style does not show in flowers or
fruits. The berries, which may be ripe by July,
often have a whitish bloom.

Beach
Edge
Forest
Meadow
Muskeg

Alaska Blueberry

Vaccinium alaskaense

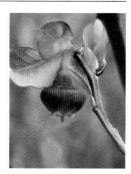

This and the following are bushes to 2 me-
ters high. In Alaska blueberry the twigs are
somewhat angled and green to light brown
(lighter in color than *V. ovalifolium*.) The
coppery-pink, urn-shaped flowers are broader
than they are long. The blue-black berry lacks
a white bloom. The style often shows in the
flowers and berries.

Beach
Edge
Forest
Meadow
Muskeg

Bog Blueberry
Bilberry

Vaccinium uliginosum

This is a much-branched low shrub, with minute hairs along the stems. The leaves are blue-green above, paler below, sometimes tinged with purple, oval to elliptic in shape, and <u>smooth at the margins</u>.

They are deciduous, turning red-purple in autumn. The flowers are urn-shaped, nodding, pink, with four lobes at the opening. The flowers appear in May. It also occurs in alpine regions where the familiar blue berries are much loved by people and bears.

Beach
Edge
Forest
Meadow
Muskeg

Bog Blueberry
Dwarf Bilberry

Vaccinium cespitosum

It is similar in stature (a low-growing shrub) to *V. uliginosum,* and both are found in bogs and alpine regions. This one has leaves that are bright green above and below, and the leaf margins have very small, gland-tipped teeth. The flowers are a bit redder and less round than the flowers of V. *uliginosum.*

Beach
Edge
Forest
Meadow
Muskeg

Bog Cranberry

Oxycoccus microcarpus
(=Vaccinium oxycoccos)

Tiny, tiny, tiny; you won't know it is there
until you search in the wet moss of bogs.
The leaves are widely spaced, evergreen, and
pointed. The flowers are pink to red, the petals directed backwards like a miniature shooting star. The red berries, nestled in a bed of
moss, look much too large for the rest of the
plant. I don't see how such a small amount
of leaf tissue can support the growth of such
large berries.

Beach
Edge
Forest
Meadow
Muskeg

FABACEAE
The Pea Family

Beach Pea

Lathyrus japonicus

It grows on gravel beaches. The compound leaves end in curly tendrils that are used to clamber over other plants. The large purple pea flowers, in one-sided clusters on a nodding stem, can be seen for much of the season, May to August. The peas are good to eat.

Beach
Edge
Forest
Meadow
Muskeg

Michael DeYoung / AlaskaStock.com

Alpine Sweetvetch
Eskimo Potato

Hedysarum alpinum

The leaves have 15-20 leaflets that are hairy on the lower surface. The flowers, arrayed on vertical stalks above the leaves, are wine/purple, more intensely colored near the tip, and deflexed (pointing downward.) The youngest flowers are at the top; older flowers and developing fruits below. This plant reaches the southern limit of its distribution around Glacier Bay, where it is abundant on glacial moraines, rocky slopes and river bars (as in the photo that adorns the cover of this book.) As one common name indicates, the roots are eaten by Native Alaskans.

Beach
Edge
Forest
Meadow
Muskeg

Nootka Lupine
Alaska Lupine

Lupinus nootkatensis

This robust herb can grow in dense stands up to a meter or so (40 inches) in height. The leaves are palmately compound, with 5 to 9 leaflets radiating from a common center and dissimilar in size. The flowers are packed in dense clusters near the top of the plant, younger above, older below. The petals are blue, often tinged with white or pink. The pea pods are black.

It is common on gravel bars and beaches. Nootka Lupine has become a common roadside weed in northern Europe. Lupines contain toxic alkaloid compounds.

Beach
Edge
Forest
Meadow
Muskeg

GENTIANACEAE
The Gentians

Look for the opposite stem leaves.

Swamp Gentian

Gentiana douglasiana

Beach
Edge
Forest
Meadow
Muskeg

This erect, hairless, perennial herb is about six inches (15 cm) or so in height and branched at the base. It has a basal leaf rosette and smaller stem leaves. The flowers are solitary or several, arising from leaf axils. The corolla is tubular, bluish at the base, flaring into five whitish lobes with two smaller folds between the lobes. It flowers in August.

Swertia

Swertia perennis

This perennial herb grows from woody
rhizomes in bogs and very wet meadows,
extending into the subalpine zone. The blue-
purple flowers are in terminal clusters. The
petals are often striped or spotted. When it
flowers in August it may be showy, but otherwise it is rather inconspicuous. It is not very
common.

Beach
Edge
Forest
Meadow
Muskeg

GERANIACEAE
The geranium or storksbill family

Northern Geranium

Geranium erianthum

This fairly stout herb reaches two feet or so in height. It has basal leaves with long petioles. They are circular in outline but lobed and toothed, with appressed hairs. The stem leaves, below the flowers, lack petioles. The sepals are quite bristly. The five large, showy petals are blue to pink-purple, with purple lines radiating from the center of the flower. There are often two flowers looking in opposite directions at 90 degrees to the erect flowering stem, above the leaves.

| Beach |
| Edge |
| Forest |
| Meadow |
| Muskeg |

GROSSULARIACEAE
The Currants

Stink Currant

Ribes bracteosum

This large shrub has a strong skunky odor.
The leaves are large, palmate, with 5 to 7
pointed lobes. There are 20 to 40 white
flowers with maroon throats arrayed along
an erect raceme. It flowers in May and early
June. The fruits are blue-black with a white
bloom, and not particularly tasty.

Beach
Edge
Forest
Meadow
Muskeg

Swamp Gooseberry
Bristly Black Currant
Black Gooseberry

Ribes lacustre

A shrub with numerous golden spines along the stem and larger spines at the leaf nodes. The spines may cause an allergic reaction in some people so be careful. The leaves are palmate, maple-like, with five deeply incised lobes, the petioles with spines. The reddish flowers are arrayed along a drooping raceme, usually in June. The fruits are dark purple, with gland-tipped hairs. They are edible but not much used.

Beach
Edge
Forest
Meadow
Muskeg

MENYANTHACEAE
The Buckbean Family

Deer-cabbage

Fauria crista-galli

The leaves are basal, roundish to kidney-shaped, and fine-dentate (toothed) along the margin. They can be easily confused with Marsh-marigold, *Caltha*, but in *Caltha* the basal lobes of the leaves usually overlap. The flowers appear in mid-season on erect stems; they have white petals that are wavy at the margins. The flowers are foul smelling, a pretty sure sign of fly-pollination.

Beach
Edge
Forest
Meadow
Muskeg

Bog Bean
Buckbean

Menyanthes trifoliata

Beach
Edge
Forest
Meadow
Muskeg

It grows in still water and very wet sites in bogs. The leaves are rubbery, consisting of three leaflets (hence *"trifoliata"*) that are held erect. The flowers are clustered on erect stems; they are white and frilly-fringed, with a not-so-pleasant aroma. It flowers in June, ahead of its relative Deer Cabbage, so they avoid competition for the pollinator service of flies.

NYMPHAEACEAE
The Pond Lily or Water Lily Family

(note that they are not lilies)

Yellow Pond Lily

Nuphar polysepalum (= N. luteum)

It is found in still water – ponds and lake margins. It has very large, rubbery, floating leaves. The enormous, globe-like, yellow flowers are solitary, floating, connected to the rhizomes by long stalks. The conspicuous globe is formed by 7-9 yellow sepals; the numerous petals are much smaller and hidden.

Beach
Edge
Forest
Meadow
Muskeg

ONAGRACEAE
The Evening Primrose Family

River Beauty

Chamerion latifolium.

Older literature will place the two fireweed species in *Epilobium*.

This is a plant of river bars, stream sides,
scree slopes, and sometimes seeming to grow
right out of the rock of fjord walls. It is <u>much
branched</u>. The blue-green leaves are opposite
below, alternate above. The showy magenta
flowers are in loose terminal clusters. When
the flowers are fertile you can see bright blue-
green pollen grains on the anthers and on the
stigma.

Beach
Edge
Forest
Meadow
Muskeg

Tall Fireweed

Chamerion angustifolium

This is Alaska's most common, or at least most conspicuous, roadside plant. It has an erect <u>unbranched</u> stem densely adorned with lance-shaped leaves. The pink-purple flowers are in a terminal spike, flowering from the base. The flowers are functionally male early, female later. Look for the blue-green pollen grains. When fireweed stops flowering, winter is upon us! Fireweed honey and syrup are both popular in Alaska.

Beach
Edge
Forest
Meadow
Muskeg

OROBANCHACEAE
The Broomrape Family

Ground Cone

Boschniakia rossica

This is a parasite on the roots of alder. It
lacks chlorophyll and looks a bit like a cluster
of large, red-brown spruce cones stuck into
the ground beneath alders. A single, inconspicuous, purple flower appears in each leaf
axil.

Beach
Edge
Forest
Meadow
Muskeg

PLANTAGINACEAE
The Plantain Family

Sea Plantain
Goose-tongue

Plantago maritima

It grows in rocky areas that are immersed at
high tide. It has clusters of linear leaves and
green-brown, membranous flowers that are
densely-packed on an erect spike. It flowers
pretty much throughout the summer season.

Beach
Edge
Forest
Meadow
Muskeg

Seashore Plantain
Alaska Plantain

Plantago macrocarpa

It is found on upper beaches and beach meadows, and thus is not quite as salt-tolerant as *P. maritima*. It is taller (20 to 40 cm) and the leaves are much broader. The flowers occur in the early summer—May and June. The young, tender leaves of both species are edible in salads or cooked like spinach.

Beach
Edge
Forest
Meadow
Muskeg

POLYGONACEAE
The Buckwheat Family

Alpine Bistort
Viviparous Knotweed

Bistorta vivipara (=Polygonum viviparum of older literature.)

This erect herb grows from a perennial rhizome. The basal leaves are narrowly oblong; the stem leaves are much smaller. The flowers are densely packed on an erect spike above the leaves. The upper flowers are white to pink. Below the flowers are asexual bulblets that can germinate to form a clone of the parent plant. It occurs in wet alpine and coastal meadows, beaches, and in bogs.

Beach
Edge
Forest
Meadow
Muskeg

Curly Dock

Rumex crispus

This plant occurs in every state of the union and in most of Canada. In coastal Alaska it is probably introduced and invasive in coastal meadows and disturbed habitats. The lance-shaped leaves are curled at the margins and crenulated. The basal leaves are broader than the stem leaves. The flowers occur in dense clusters; they give rise to red fruits.

Beach
Edge
Forest
Meadow
Muskeg

PORTULACACEAE
The Purslane Family

Spring Beauty
Siberian Miners'
Lettuce

Claytonia (= Montia) sibirica

This is a somewhat succulent annual of moist spots on the upper beach and moist meadows near the coast. Look for the two opposite stem leaves under the flowering stalks. The flowers vary from white to pale pink to blue-purple, with five petals that are notched. The edible leaves make a fine salad.

Beach
Edge
Forest
Meadow
Muskeg

PRIMULACEAE
The Primrose Family

Starflower

Trientalis arctica

This is a small perennial herb arising from
rhizomes. It has one to three white flowers,
often with seven sepals and petals (that is an
unusual number), each on a short, wiry, red
stalk. A whorl of 5-6 simple and entire leaves
occurs where the flowering stems diverge. It
is widely distributed in wet forests, meadows,
and bogs.

Beach
Edge
Forest
Meadow
Muskeg

Shootingstar

Dodecatheon pulchellum

The distinctive magenta flowers point downward. The petals are swept backwards like, well, a shooting star. It is quite commmon, growing in clumps in moist meadows.

Shootingstars have a remarkable system of "buzz pollination." Vibration from the wings and flight muscles of bees (in the proper frequency) cause the release of pollen. Thus, the plant releases pollen only when an appropriate pollinator is available.

Beach
Edge
Forest
Meadow
Muskeg

Sea Milkwort

Glaux maritima

This mat-forming plant grows in the intertidal zone where it is immersed at each high
tide. The somewhat succulent shiny green
leaves are opposite. The flowers are solitary
in leaf axils, purple in the center. It has five
pale pink, petal-like sepals, but no true petals.

Beach
Edge
Forest
Meadow
Muskeg

PYROLACEAE
The Wintergreen Family

Shy Maiden
Single Delight
Wax Flower

Moneses (Pyrola) uniflora

This small plant occurs in the deep forest
where little light reaches the forest floor. It
has a basal rosette of roundish leaves and a
single white, waxy flower that points downward demurely, hence "shy maiden".

Beach
Edge
Forest
Meadow
Muskeg

Pink Pyrola
Liverleaf Wintergreen

Beach
Edge
Forest
Meadow
Muskeg

Pyrola asarifolia

The leaves are mostly basal, round to ovate, leathery, and often purple on the lower side. It has a flowering stalk (raceme) with showy pink to red flowers in late June and July.

One-sided Wintergreen

Orthilia (Pyrola) secunda

It grows from a much-branched rhizome.
The leaves are basal, more pointed and
smaller than *P. asarifolia,* and finely-toothed.
The greenish to white urn-shaped flowers are
densely packed <u>on one side</u> only of the stem.
The flowering stem commonly bends so the
flowers are arrayed horizontally, not vertically. The style extends well beyond the throat
of the corolla.

Beach
Edge
Forest
Meadow
Muskeg

Emily Mount

American Pinesap

Monotropa hypopithys

This widely-distributed plant occurs as clusters of fleshy stems. It is usually described as saprophytic (living from dead matter) but it is probably mycotrophic (depending on a fungal associate for its nutrition.) In either case, it lacks chlorophyll and is yellow to pink in color, drying to black. The waxy white to yellowish flowers occur in terminal clusters that are usually nodding. It is found in dense forests. Since it lacks chlorophyll it can do just fine in the dim light of the forest floor.

Beach
Edge
Forest
Meadow
Muskeg

RANUNCULACEAE
The Crowfoot or Buttercup Family

These often contain poisonous compounds.

Baneberry

Actaea rubra

This tall herb has compound leaves that are two to three times divided into three, with each leaflet pointed and coarsely toothed. Small white flowers atop wiry stems produce clusters of <u>deadly poisonous</u> red or, less commonly, white berries. It flowers May to June.

Beach
Edge
Forest
Meadow
Muskeg

Three-leaved Goldthread

Coptis trifolia

This small, delicate perennial herb flowers most conspicuously in bogs; it is also found in the forest floor. The leaves are shiny green and divided into three leaflets (hence "*trifolia*") that are toothed. The five white things that look like petals are actually sepals; the petals are reduced to orange-tipped filaments that alternate with the sepals. It is commonly the first flower of the season to brighten the bogs (mid-May), shortly after the flowers of its relative, fern-leaved goldthread, appear in the forest floor.

| Beach |
| Edge |
| Forest |
| Meadow |
| Muskeg |

Fern-leaf Goldthread

Coptis asplenifolia

This delicate herb grows from gold-colored roots, hence the common name. The leaves are evergreen and fern-like. One to three (often two) very small and delicate white flowers (right) appear on leafless stalks very early in the season (April to May). They look not unlike a dead spider on a stick. The fruits form a conspicuous ring of up to 12 capsules spreading from an erect stem (upper right); a seed is dispersed each time the capsule is hit by a raindrop. It is a slow colonizer and hence an indicator species of old-growth forest. The leaves are an important winter food for black-tailed deer.

| Beach |
| Edge |
| Forest |
| Meadow |
| Muskeg |

White Marsh-marigold

Caltha leptosepala

The leaves look very much like those of the
yellow march-marigold. The two species occur in similar habitats and are easily mistaken
when not in flower. In flower they are unmistakable: White marsh-marigold has from six
to twelve white sepals that are often tinged
with purple at the base.

Beach
Edge
Forest
Meadow
Muskeg

Yellow Marsh-marigold

Caltha palustris

The leaves are roundish, rubbery and fine-toothed, with the basal lobes overlapping. A single showy yellow flower with no petals but five to eight bright yellow sepals rises above the leaves. It is found in very wet meadows with slow running or seeping water. The young leaves are reputed to be tasty, but they contain poisons that must be destroyed by cooking.

Beach
Edge
Forest
Meadow
Muskeg

Western Buttercup

Ranunculus occidentalis

The basal leaves usually have three wedge-shaped divisions; the stem leaves are smaller and more dissected. The flowers are bright butter-yellow. They can be found throughout the summer season. It is a common plant of moist meadows.

Beach
Edge
Forest
Meadow
Muskeg

Western Columbine

Aquilegia formosa

A medium-sized herb. The leaves are basal, twice divided into threes, pale below. The flowers are unmistakable, with many long yellow anthers and five long red spurs that invite the attention of hummingbirds. It is often found in vertical rock faces.

Beach
Edge
Forest
Meadow
Muskeg

ROSACEAE
The Rose Family

Goatsbeard

Aruncus dioicus

This shrub has compound leaves, the leaflets
sharply toothed and pointed. The tiny white
flowers are densely packed on long, branched
spikes above the foliage. Male flowers, bearing stamens, and female flowers, bearing
pistils, are on separate plants.

Beach
Edge
Forest
Meadow
Muskeg

Yellow Dryas

Dryas drummondii

This mat-forming woody plant is found on river gravel bars, recently deglaciated slopes, and rocky coasts, from sea level to the alpine zone. The leaf margins have rounded teeth between the veins. The flowers are stalked, nodding, and never open fully. There are 8 to 10 sepals with dark glandular hairs, and a similar number of yellow petals. The seeds are attached to feathery plumes for dispersal by the wind. *Dryas* has nitrogen-fixing bacteria associated with the roots; it is important in plant succession following deglaciation by introducing nitrogen to the newly exposed soils.

Beach
Edge
Forest
Meadow
Muskeg

Beach Strawberry

Fragaria chiloensis

Beach
Edge
Forest
Meadow
Muskeg

This low growing plant of coastal meadows creeps over the ground on red runners. The leaves are three-foliate and leathery. The flowers are white with five sepals and petals. They appear in late May. The fruits are little red flavor-bombs.

Pacific Crab Apple

Malus (= Pyrus) fusca

This is a small deciduous tree with abundant
white blossoms in spring. The apples are
small and tart; you probably won't like them.

Beach
Edge
Forest
Meadow
Muskeg

Pacific Silverweed

Potentilla anserina

It is common along shores and tidal meadows, often immersed at high tide, growing from runners. The leaves are pinnately compound. The leaflets increase in size distally; they are toothed and silver-pubescent below. The flowers with five bright yellow petals are single, on long stalks.

Beach
Edge
Forest
Meadow
Muskeg

Villous Cinquefoil

Potentilla villosa

It grows right out of rocks just above the beach or shore. The leaves are three-foliate, white-hairy beneath and along the margins. The flowers are yellow. The petals do not meet at the base so the sepals show through between the petal bases.

Beach
Edge
Forest
Meadow
Muskeg

Marsh Cinquefoil

Comarum palustre
(= Potentilla palustris)

This herbaceous plant is always found growing in shallow fresh water. The leaves are
pinnately compound with five to seven leaflets that are coarsely toothed. The five long,
pointed sepals are greenish-purple, alternat-
ing with five shorter dark brownish-purple
petals. As in other roses, there are numerous
stamens and pistils. The flowers have a foul
odor, the better to attract carrion flies as pol-
linators.

Emily Mount

Beach
Edge
Forest
Meadow
Muskeg

Large-leaf Avens

Geum macrophyllum

This common, coarse herb has large compound basal leaves with long petioles. The leaflets are round in outline, lobed, and hairy below; the terminal leaflet is much the largest. The stem leaves are sessile (without petioles), sharply lobed, and dentate. The flowers appear in June. The yellow petals do not meet at the base. The anthers are orange. The fruits are clusters of hairy nutlets; each is attached to a long, red style that is hooked at the tip, the better to catch on to passing animals (wool socks work just fine) and achieve seed dispersal.

Beach
Edge
Forest
Meadow
Muskeg

Dwarf Nagoonberry

Rubus arcticus

This low-growing plant comes from a woody rootstalk. The leaves are somewhat leathery, tripartite, and fine-toothed. It has magenta flowers. The fruit are tasty but small, with few drupelets. It occurs in moist meadows.

Beach
Edge
Forest
Meadow
Muskeg

Five-leaved Bramble

Rubus pedatus

This is a common trailing plant of the forest floor, growing in moss. The leaves are long-stalked and palmately divided into five leaflets, hence the common name. The flowers are white. The fruit consist of 1 to 6 red druplets.

| Beach |
| Edge |
| Forest |
| Meadow |
| Muskeg |

Cloudberry

Rubus chamaemorus

This low-growing plant is restricted to bogs. The leaves are leathery, roundish, and palmately-lobed. The single flower above the leaves has five white petals and five hairy sepals. Male and female flowers are on separate plants. It flowers in May and early June. The ripe fruit is yellow to orange and juicy, but seedy. They are good on vanilla ice cream. Cloudberries are highly prized in Scandinavia, but they are not much eaten here.

| Beach |
| Edge |
| Forest |
| Meadow |
| Muskeg |

Salmonberry

Rubus spectabilis

A large shrub of forest edge. The leaves are distinctly three-foliate, the two lateral leaflets smaller than the terminal, and lobed. If you take away the terminal leaflet you have a butterfly. The magenta flowers appear early in the season. They are usually looking downward. The fruit is yellow to red, even on the same bush, and quite tasty.

Beach
Edge
Forest
Meadow
Muskeg

Thimbleberry

Rubus parviflorus

This is another shrub of forest edges. The large leaves are maple-shaped. The open white flowers appear later than salmonberry, with which it often grows. The fruits are red and easily come off the core, thimble-fashion. They are reminiscent of raspberries and very tasty.

Beach
Edge
Forest
Meadow
Muskeg

Sitka Burnet

Sanguisorba canadensis ssp. *latifolia*
(= S. sitchensis)

The basal leaves are pinnately compound, the leaflets ovate (oval shaped) and dentate (with teeth along the margins.) The small flowers are densely packed onto erect spikes rising above the leaves, appearing white and shaggy because of the very long stamens. The young leaves are good in salads.

Beach
Edge
Forest
Meadow
Muskeg

Douglas Spirea Hardhack

Spiraea douglasii

When in flower (July and August) this deciduous shrub is told by its conical clusters of pink to rose flowers extending above the foliage. The leaves are elliptic to oblong, and toothed in the outer half. It grows in wet soil along forest margins, and especially around streams and lakes. It reaches the northern extent of its distribution in Southeast Alaska

Beach
Edge
Forest
Meadow
Muskeg

RUBIACEAE
The Madder Family

Cleavers

Galium aparine

This sprawling herb occurs in shady spots
on the upper beach. Whorls of 6-8 linear
leaves are evenly spaced along the stem. The
leaves and stem have tiny, hooked bristles, so
they stick to your clothing. The small white
flowers in leaf axils are conspicuously four-
petaled.

Beach
Edge
Forest
Meadow
Muskeg

SAXIFRAGACEAE
The Saxifrage Family

Alumroot
Alpine Heuchera

Heuchera glabra.

Like many saxifrage species this plant seems to grow right out of the rocks, especially in the mist zone around waterfalls. The basal leaves are shiny, lobed and toothed; stem leaves are small. The numerous tiny white flowers are in loose arrays on wiry stems above the leaves.

| Beach |
| Edge |
| Forest |
| Meadow |
| Muskeg |

Margaret Manson

Foamflower

Tiarella trifoliata

It has basal leaves and a few stem leaves, each with three leaflets.   They are irregularly lobed and more pointed than the superficially similar (in the absence of flowers) Three-leaved goldthread (*Coptis trifolia*, p. 174). Many tiny delicate white flowers are arrayed along a wire-like stalk well above the leaves. The ten stamens extend well beyond the petals.

Beach
Edge
Forest
Meadow
Muskeg

Purple Saxifrage
Purple Mountain Saxifrage

Saxifraga oppositifolia

This is a very widely distributed plant of arctic and alpine tundra that occasionally reaches steep rock walls above beaches. It forms dense mats, with the leaves very tightly packed in four rows. The large and showy magenta flowers appear very early in the spring and are usually done by June.

Beach
Edge
Forest
Meadow
Muskeg

SCROPHULARIACEAE
The Figwort Family:
Snapdragons et al.

Red Paintbrush

Castilleja miniata

This plant of coastal meadows has small, inconspicuous flowers that are surrounded by showy red-tipped bracts (modified leaves.) It is hemiparasitic on the roots of other plants. That is, it takes water and nutrients from the host but it is capable of photosynthesis to make its own sugar.

Beach
Edge
Forest
Meadow
Muskeg

Unalaska Paintbrush

Castilleja unalaschensis

This is similar to red paintbrush and grows in similar meadow habitats, but the bracts surrounding the flowers are yellow rather than red.

Both paintbrush species often have spittlebugs attacking where the leaves join the stem.

Beach
Edge
Forest
Meadow
Muskeg

Yellow Rattle
Rattlebox

Rhinanthus minor

This is an annual herb, so don't look for it
early in the season. The leaves are opposite,
stalkless, lance-shaped, and coarsely toothed.
The flowers are yellow. The sepals are fused
into an inflated, flattened balloon that makes
the plant unmistakable.

| Beach |
| Edge |
| Forest |
| Meadow |
| Muskeg |

Yellow Monkey-flower

Mimulus guttatus

This low herb may be either annual or perennial. The lower leaves are on petioles; the upper leaves are sessile, and opposite along the stem. The "snapdragon" flowers are bright yellow; the lower lip is much longer than the upper lip, and often marked with red or purple.

Beach
Edge
Forest
Meadow
Muskeg

Whorled Lousewort

Pedicularis verticillata.

The common name comes from the whorl of leaves that surround the stem. The basal leaves are on petioles; the stem leaves are sessile (lacking petioles). The leaves are deeply lobed and the lobes are toothed. The rose-pink flowers are densely packed all around the stem, in the familiar snapdragon shape with a large helmet. It is mainly a plant of higher elevations but it is sometimes found in coastal meadows.

Beach
Edge
Forest
Meadow
Muskeg

VIOLACEAE: The Violet Family

They have showy flowers with five petals that are asymmetrical.

Stream Violet
Yellow Wood Violet

Beach
Edge
Forest
Meadow
Muskeg

Viola glabella

It has heart-shaped leaves and a single yellow flower; the lower three petals have purple-brown lines. It is found in moist, shady spots and under other vegetation. It flowers early in season, beginning in May.

Dwarf Marsh Violet

Viola epipsila

This violet grows from long, thin rhizomes
and creeping stolons. The leaves are heart-
shaped. The flowers are on long stalks; they
are pale lilac with dark veins on the lower
three petals. Young leaves and buds can be
eaten raw in salads. It occurs in wet meadows
and along streams.

Beach
Edge
Forest
Meadow
Muskeg

Alaska Violet

Viola langsdorffii

It is without stolons; the leaves arise from the apex of a thick rhizome. The petals are dark blue-purple.

Beach
Edge
Forest
Meadow
Muskeg

Table C. Plant Relationships   207

FUNGI				Fungi
LICHENS				Lichens
PLANTS Non-Vascular (lack specialized conducting tissue)				Mosses Liverworts
PLANTS **Vascular** (have xylem and phloem conducting tissue)	**NON-FLOWER-ING PLANTS** (reproduce by spores)			Equisetaceae Lycopodiaceae Polypodiaceae
	FLOWERING PLANTS (reproduce by seeds)	**GYMNO-SPERMAE** Cone-Bearing Plants (seeds borne naked on the surface of scales.		Pinaceae Cupressaceae
		ANGIO-SPERMAE (seeds develop within a carpel)	**MONOCOTY-LEDONAE** One seed leaf; leaves with parallel veins; flower parts in 3s and 6s.	Araceae Cyperaceae Iridaceae Juncaginaceae Liliaceae Orchidaceae Poaceae Scheuchzeriaceae
			DICOTYLE-DONAE Two seed leaves with net veins; flower parts commonly in 4s and 5s.	Aceraceae Apiaceae Araliaceae Asteraceae Betulaceae Boraginaceae Brassicaceae Campanulaceae Caprifoliaceae Caryophyllaceae Chenopodiaceae Cornaceae Droseraceae Empetraceae Ericaceae Fabaceae Gentianaceae Grossulariaceae Menyanthaceae Nymphaeaceae Onagraceae Orobanchaceae Plantaginaceae Polygonaceae Portulacaceae Primulaceae Pyrolaceae Ranunculaceae Rosaceae Rubiaceae Saxifragaceae Scrophulariaceae Violaceae

Table D. Plant Identification Key

The plant species in this book are arranged by Family, in alphabetical sequence. Even if plant families are unfamiliar to you, as long as you can see flower color and count the petals, this table should lead you to the most likely suspects. In case you are uncertain about the color or or arrangement of the flower, the plant species are listed under the several possibilities.

FLOWERS	White/Ivory	Yellow	Blue/Purple	Red/Pink/ Orange	Green
3 Petals					
Iridaceae			Blue Flag Iris – *Iris setosa* (plus 3 conspicuous sepals.)		
4 Petals					
Brassicaceae	Little Western Bittercress *Cardamine oligosperma*				
Cornaceae	Dwarf Dogwood *Cornus canadensis* (the 4 white things are petaloid bracts, not petals.)				
	Bog Bunchberry; Swedish bunchberry *Cornus suecica* (the flowers as above.)				

Family			
Ericaceae			Bog Cranberry *Oxycoccus microcarpus*
Onagraceae	River Beauty *Chamerion latifolium*		River Beauty *Chamerion latifolium*
	Tall Fireweed *Chamerion angustifolium*		Tall Fireweed *Chamerion angustifolium*
Rubiaceae	Cleavers – *Galium aparine*		
5 Petals			
Aceraceae			Douglas Maple *Acer glabrum*
Boraginaceae		Oysterleaf *Mertensia maritima*	
Campanulaceae		Harebell *Campanula rotundifolia.*	
Caryophyllaceae	Beach Greens *Honckenya peploides*		Beach Greens - *Honckenya peploides*
	Field Chickweed *Cerastium arvense*		

Family			
Droseraceae	Round-leaved Sundew *Drosera rotundifolia*		
	Great Sundew *Drosera anglica*		
Ericaceae			Bog Cranberry *Vaccinium oxycoccos*
Gentianaceae	Swamp Gentian *Gentiana douglasiana*	Swertia *Swertia perennis*	
Geraniaceae		NorthernGeranium *Geranium erianthum*	
Grossulariaceae	Stink Currant *Ribes bracteosum*		Bristly Black Currant – *Ribes lacustre*
Menyanthaceae	Deer-cabbage *Fauria crista-galli*		
	Bog Bean *Menyanthes trifoliata*		
Portulacaceae	Spring Beauty *Claytonia siberica*		Spring Beauty *Claytonia siberica*
Primulaceae	Sea Milkwort - *Glaux maritima*. (These are sepals that look like petals.)		
Pyrolaceae	Shy Maiden *Moneses uniflora*		Pink Pyrola *Pyrola asarifolia*

211

Ranunculaceae	Three-leaved Goldthread *Coptis trifolia* (Again, they are sepals, not petals.)	Western Buttercup *Ranunculus occidentalis*		
Rosaceae	Beach Strawberry *Fragaria chiloensis*	Yellow Dryas *Dryas drummondii*		
	Pacific Crab Apple *Malus fusca*	Pacific Silverweed *Potentilla anserina*	Marsh Cinquefoil *Comarum palustre*	
	Five-leaved Bramble *Rubus pedatus*	Villous Cinquefoil *Potentilla villosa*	Salmonberry *Rubus spectabilis*	Salmonberry *Rubus spectabilis*
	Cloudberry *Rubus chamaemorus*	Large-leaf Avens *Geum macrophyllum*		
	Thimbleberry *Rubus parviflorus*			
Saxifragaceae	Foamflower *Tiarella trifoliata*		Purple Saxifrage *Saxifraga oppositifolia*	
	Alumroot; Alpine Heuchera - *Heuchera glabra*			
Violaceae	Yellow Wood Violet - *Viola glabella*	Dwarf Marsh Violet – *Viola epipsila*		
		Alaska Violet *Viola langsdorffii*		

6 Petals				
Liliaceae	Queen's Cup *Clintonia uniflora*	Sticky False Asphodel *Triantha glutinosa*	Chocolate Lily *Fritillaria camschatcensis*	Clasping Twisted Stalk - *Streptopus amplexifolius*
Rosaceae			Dwarf Nagoonberry - *Rubus arcticus* (There may be 7 petals.)	Dwarf Nagoonberry - *Rubus arcticus* (There may be 7 petals.)
More than 6 petals (or ray flowers of composites)				
Asteraceae	Beach Groundsel *Senecio pseudoarnica*	Douglas Aster *Symphyotrichum subspicatum*		
Nymphaeaceae	Yellow Pond Lily *Nuphar polysepalum* (actually, they are sepals that look like petals.)			
Primulaceae	Starflower *Trientalis arctica* (commonly 7 or 8 petals.)			

213

Family				
Ranunculaceae	White Marsh-marigold *Caltha leptosepala* (it can have 5 to 8 white petaloid sepals.)	Yellow Marsh-marigold – *Caltha palustris* (it can have 5 to 8 yellow petaloid sepals.)		
Rosaceae			Dwarf Nagoonberry - *Rubus arcticus*	Dwarf Nagoonberry - *Rubus arcticus*
Petals united into a tube or bell				
Boraginaceae			Oysterleaf *Mertensia maritima*	
Campanulaceae			Harebell - *Campanula rotundifolia*	
Caprifoliaceae				Twinflower *Linnaea borealis*
Ericaceae	Bearberry; kinnikinnick *Arctostaphylos uva-ursi*			Bog Rosemary *Andromeda polifolia*
				Bearberry; kinnikinnick – *Arctostaphylos uva-ursi*
				Bog Laurel *Kalmia polifolia*
				False Azalea *Menziesia ferruginea*

	Red Huckleberry *Vaccinium parvifolium*	Alaska Blueberry *Vaccinium alaskaense*	Early Blueberry *Vaccinium ovalifolium*	Lingonberry *Vaccinium vitis-idaea*	Bog Blueberry *Vaccinium uliginosum*	Bog Blueberry; dwarf bilberry *Vaccinium cespitosum*	Rosy Twisted Stalk *Streptopus roseus*	Clasping Twisted Stalk - *Streptopus amplexifolius*	One-sided Wintergreen *Orthilia secunda*
Liliaceae									
Pyrolaceae	One-sided Wintergreen *Orthilia secunda*								
Rosaceae		Yellow Dryas *Dryas drummondii.*							

Flowers markedly irregular

Family			
Fabaceae		Beach Pea *Lathyrus japonicus*	
		Nootka Lupine *Lupinus nootkatensis*	
Orchidaceae	Rattlesnake-Plantain *Goodyera oblongifolia*	Heart-leaved Twayblade *Listera cordata*	Heart-leaved Twayblade *Listera cordata*
	White Bog-orchid *Platanthera dilatata*	Fairy Slipper; Calypso Orchid *Calypso bulbosa*	Northwestern Twayblade *Listera caurina*
		Coral-root *Corallorhiza maculata*	Slender Bog orchid; Rein Orchid *Platanthera stricta*
Ericaceae			Bog Cranberry *Oxycoccus microcarpus*
Primulaceae		Shootingstar *Dodecatheon pulchellum*	
Ranunculaceae	Fern-leaf Goldthread *Coptis asplenifolia*		Western Columbine *Aquilegia formosa*

Family			
Scrophularia-ceae	Unalaska Paint-brush - *Castilleja unalaschensis* (The yellow structures are modified leaves, not petals.)		Red Paintbrush *Castilleja miniata* (The red structures are modified leaves, not petals.)
	Yellow Rattle; Rattlebox *Rhinanthus minor*		
	Yellow Monkey-flower *Mimulus guttatus*		

Flowers occurring in more or less dense flowering heads

Family			
Araceae	Skunk Cabbage *Lysichiton americanum*		
Araliaceae	Devil's Club *Oplopanax horridus*		
Apiaceae	Beach Lovage *Ligusticum scoticum*		
	Cow Parsnip *Heracleum lanatum*		
	Seacoast Angelica *Angelica lucida*		
Asteraceae	Yarrow *Achillea millefolium*		Yarrow *Achillea millefolium*

Family			
Betulaceae	Red Alder *Alnus rubra*		
	Sitka Alder *Alnus sinuata*		
Caprifoliaceae	Highbush Cranberry *Viburnum edule*		
	Red Elderberry *Sambucus racemosa*		
Ericaceae	Labrador Tea *Ledum groenlandicum*		
Chenopodiaceae			Spearscale *Atriplex patula*
Cornaceae	Red-Osier Dogwood *Cornus stolonifera*		
Liliaceae	False Lily-of-the-Valley *Maianthemum dilatatum*		False Hellebore *Veratrum viride*
Polygonaceae	Alpine Bistort *Bistorta vivipara*		
Ranunculaceae	Baneberry *Actaea rubra.*		
Rosaceae	Goatsbeard *Aruncus dioicus*	Douglas Spirea *Spiraea douglasii*	
	Sitka Burnet *Sanguisorba canadensis*		

Index

Useful References

Armstrong, Robert H. and Marge Hermans. 2004. *Southeast Alaska's Natural World.* Anchorage, Alaska: Todd Communications.

Brodo, Irwin M., Sylvia D. Sharnoff and Stephen Sharnoff. 2001. *Lichens of North America.* New Haven and London: Yale University Press.

Durbin, Kathie. 2005. *Tongass: Pulp Politics and the fight for the Alaska Rain Forest.* Second Edition. Corvallis: Oregon State University Press.

Feuerer, T. (ed.), 2008: Checklists of lichens and lichenicolous fungi. Version 1 June 2008. - http://www.checklists.de

Hall, Judy K. 1995. *Native Plants of Southeast Alaska.* Juneau, Alaska: Windy Ridge Publishing.

Hultén, Eric. 1968. *Flora of Alaska and Neighboring Territories.* Stanford, California: Stanford University Press.

Ketchum, Robert G. and Carey D. Ketchum. 1994. *The Tongass: Alaska's Vanishing Rainforest.* New York: the Aperture Foundation.

Laursen, Gary A. and Rodney D. Seppelt. 2009. *Common Interior Alaska Cryptogams: Fungi, Lichenicolous Fungi, Lichenized Fungi, Slime Molds, Mosses, and Liverworts.* Fairbanks, Alaska; University of Alaska Press.

Milnus, Susan. 2001. A fly called aiyaiyai. *Science News,* May 26, 2001.

O'Clair, Rita M., Robert H. Armstrong, and Richard Carstensen. 1992. *The Nature of Southeast Alaska.* Anchorage and Seattle: Alaska Northwest Books.

Parker, Harriette. 1994. *Alaska's Mushrooms: a practical guide.* Anchorage, Seattle, and Portland: Alaska Northwest Books.

Pratt, Verna. 1990. *Field Guide to Alaskan Wildflowers.* Anchorage: Alaskakrafts Publishing.

Pojar, Jim and Andy MacKinnon. 1994. *Plants of the Pacific Northwest Coast: Washington, Oregon, British Columbia, and Alaska.* Lone Pine Publishing.

Sept, J. Duane. 2006. *Common Mushrooms of the Northwest: Alaska, Western Canada, and the Northwestern United States.* Sechelt, British Columbia: Calypso Publishing.

Shulski, Martha and Gerd Wendler. 2007. *The Climate of Alaska.* Fairbanks, Alaska: University of Alaska Press.

Stowell, Harold H. 2006. *Geology of Southeast Alaska: Rock and Ice in Motion.* Fairbanks: University of Alaska Press.

Viereck, Leslie A. and Elbert L. Little. 2007. *Alaska Trees and Shrubs, Second Edition.* With contributions by David F. Murray and George W. Argus. Fairbanks, Alaska: University of Alaska Press.

Witt, Dale H., Janet E. Marsh and Robin B. Bovey. 1988. *Mosses, Lichens, and Ferns of Northwest North America.* Lone Pine Publishing.